ROSE ELL[...]
MOTHER AND B[...]

A vegetarian since the age of thre[...] eaten meat, but loves the scope which vegetarian cookery gives for imagination and creativity. She contributes to the national press, is in great demand as a cookery demonstrator, broadcasts on radio and television, and is the bestselling author of several vegetarian cookery books.

In addition to this, Rose is a professional astrologer and, with her husband, runs a computerized personal astrological service which includes personality profiles, compatibility comparisons and yearly forecasts. (For more details, please send SAE to Rose Elliot, PO Box 16, Eastleigh SO5 6BH.)

The baby on the front cover is Rose's first grandchild, Mark Adam, at 8 months, son of her eldest daughter Katy, and Gordon, and a fourth generation vegetarian.

Also by Rose Elliot

The Bean Book
Beanfeast
Cheap and Easy
Gourmet Vegetarian Cooking
The New Simply Delicious
Not Just a Load of Old Lentils
Rose Elliot's Book of Breads
Rose Elliot's Book of Cakes
Rose Elliot's Book of Fruits
Rose Elliot's Book of Pasta
Rose Elliot's Book of Salads
Rose Elliot's Book of Savoury Flans and Pies
Rose Elliot's Book of Vegetables
Vegetarian Dishes of the World
Your Very Good Health
Complete Vegetarian Cookbook
Rose Elliot's Vegetarian Cookery (hardback)
The Supreme Vegetarian (paperback)
The Green Age Diet

Rose Elliot's

Mother and Baby Book

Thorsons
An Imprint of HarperCollins*Publishers*

Thorsons
An Imprint of HarperCollins*Publishers*
77–85 Fulham Palace Road,
Hammersmith, London W6 8JB

First published as a Fontana Original under the title
Rose Elliot's Vegetarian Mother and Baby Book 1984
Published by Fontana under this title 1989
Thorsons edition 1993

2 4 6 8 9 7 5 3 1

A catalogue record for this book is
available from the British Library

ISBN 0 7225 2993 7

Printed in Great Britain by
HarperCollins Manufacturing Glasgow

Contents

Author's Note   6
Acknowledgements   7

PART I

Introduction   11
1 Diet for a Healthy Pregnancy   13
2 Pregnancy and Preparations for the Birth   35
3 Birth and the First Few Days   51
4 Coping in the Early Days, 0–3 Months   61
5 The Baby, 3–6 Months   72
6 The Baby, 6–12 Months   77
7 The Baby, 12–24 Months   92

PART II

Introduction   105
Drinks   107
Soups   114
Salads   119
Packed Meals   129
Freezer Dishes   135
Quick Main Meals   152
Puddings   181
Cakes, Biscuits and Sweets   192
Baby Foods   207

Useful Addresses   213
Further Reading   214
Index   217

Author's Note

Like all writers of books about babies, I had to face the problem of what pronoun to use when referring to the baby. Determined not to be sexist, I started by calling the baby 'it'. But that didn't sound right, so in line with a number of recent baby-care books – and since I myself have three daughters – I eventually settled on 'she'. To mothers of baby sons, I apologize if this seems inappropriate, and hope you'll mentally read 'he' instead.

Acknowledgements

I'd like to express my love and gratitude to my mother, Joan Hodgson, whose mothering was the pattern and model for my own; and to my husband and three daughters, without whom this book certainly wouldn't have been written. My grateful thanks, too, to the Vegetarian Society for encouraging me to write, and then publishing, *Rose Elliot's Vegetarian Baby Book*, and to Fontana for urging me to rewrite and expand that original small book into this present one. I would also like to thank Dr Alan Long for reading through and commenting on my section on protein; my agent, Vivienne Schuster, and my publisher, Helen Fraser, for their enthusiasm and helpful suggestions; and especially Gill Thorn, my antenatal teacher when I had Claire and dear friend ever since, for opening her library to me, and for reading right through the first half of the book and making numerous helpful and constructive comments which have been incorporated.

Part I

Introduction

Ever since my third baby was born, five years ago, people have been urging me to write a book about feeding a vegetarian baby. So, in 1981 I wrote *Rose Elliot's Vegetarian Baby Book* for the Vegetarian Society. Then my publisher asked me if I could expand that small book to cover the subject in more detail and take in other aspects of baby care as well as the nutritional one. This book is the result. I must say it has been a much more demanding (and enjoyable) project than I envisaged. It has been almost like having another baby as I mentally relived the excitement and morning sickness of pregnancy, the pain and ecstasy of giving birth, the joy of breast-feeding and the exhaustion of broken nights. I have tried to remember and record all the tips and information which I found helpful – and the things which I would have found helpful if only I'd known about them at the time! So this book is rooted firmly in practical experience, and as such I sincerely hope it will be useful to other vegetarian and vegan parents and parents-to-be – and perhaps to some non-vegetarian ones, too.

1 Diet for a Healthy Pregnancy

Producing healthy children is one of the most important – and certainly most responsible – things which most of us will do in a lifetime. Considering this, many people – myself included – take on the responsibility in a very carefree way. Now, increasingly, however, the emphasis is being placed on preparation for pregnancy and childbirth, with particular attention to diet: healthy parents produce a healthy baby.

The question of diet is a particularly important one for vegetarian/vegan parents and parents-to-be. If you're vegetarian/vegan and pregnant or planning to start a family in the near future, you may well wonder whether such a diet can supply all the nutrients necessary for producing a healthy baby. The answer is that both a vegetarian and a vegan diet can supply all the essential nutrients, and it may encourage you to know that vigorous, lively fifth generation vegetarian and vegan babies are now being born. It is useful, however, to know some facts about nutrition and to be aware of the vegetarian/vegan sources of the essential nutrients, and that is what we shall consider in this chapter.

First, perhaps, it would be helpful to explain what is usually meant by 'vegetarian' and 'vegan' diets. A vegetarian diet means one which excludes meat, fish and poultry and products derived from these, such as meat stock and fats (lard, dripping and suet, for example), and gelatine, but includes eggs, milk and other dairy produce. A vegan diet is stricter and excludes all animal produce.

When considering a vegetarian or vegan diet from the point of view of producing and nurturing healthy babies, we have to look especially at how the protein requirements can be met, and where adequate supplies of minerals, such as iron, calcium, magnesium and zinc, and vitamins, in particular the B group, can be found.

Protein

Protein requirements increase during the last few months of pregnancy, rising from an average 55g a day to 60g, and 70g during lactation. These higher requirements can easily be met by both a normal vegetarian and vegan diet.

It's important to remember that all cereals, as well as fruits and vegetables, contain some protein in addition to that obtained from the high-protein foods. Although the quantities may be quite small and the proteins low in some amino acids, taken at a meal in conjunction with other proteins they considerably boost the day's protein total. For instance, a 225-g (8-oz) serving of cooked broccoli supplies around 8g of protein; a medium-sized (225-g/8-oz) potato and two slices of wholemeal bread each add another 5g; while one 100-g (3½-oz) apple and one 200-g (7-oz) orange together add on another 1.4g. If you add that to 275ml (½ pint) skim or soya milk, which supplies 10g of protein, you will see that the total comes to 29.4g. That's around half the daily amount needed, without really trying, before adding in any of the main dishes of the day. It's just as easy to make up the remaining 30g of protein by choosing three items from the following list of foods which each supply around 10g of protein, or two from this list and two from the next list which each supply around 5g:

Foods supplying approx. 10g protein
200g (7 oz) tofu (bean curd)
40g (1½ oz) Cheddar cheese
275ml (½ pint) skim or soya milk
50g (scant 2 oz) almonds (weighed without shells)
50g (scant 2 oz) cashew nuts (weighed without shells)
50g (scant 2 oz) sesame seeds
50g (scant 2 oz) sunflower or pumpkin seeds

70g (2½ oz) brazil nuts (weighed without shells)
100g (3½ oz) walnuts (weighed without shells)
35g (1¼ oz) peanuts (weighed without shells)
40g (1½ oz) peanut butter
50g (2 oz) butter beans (uncooked weight)
50g (2 oz) haricot beans (uncooked weight)
50g (2 oz) lentils (uncooked weight)
20g (¾ oz) low-fat soya flour
75g (3 oz) cottage cheese
200g (7 oz) low-fat natural yoghurt
1 large egg*

Foods supplying approx. 5g protein
1 medium-sized (225g/8 oz) potato
2 slices (50g/2 oz) wholemeal bread
50g (2 oz) brown rice (uncooked weight)
40g (1¼ oz) oats
50g (2 oz) pasta (uncooked weight)
40g (1½ oz) Weetabix
50g (scant 2 oz) Shredded Wheat
50g (2 oz) wholemeal flour
40g (1½ oz) muesli mix

  *A large egg only comes to 7–8g but I've included it because protein in this form is very easily used by the body.

So you will see that you can complete your day's protein total by having, say, a bowl of muesli for breakfast, a cottage cheese salad or bowl of lentil soup at lunchtime, and a nut or red bean savoury in the evening (see recipe section). If in addition you have some yoghurt for pudding, or a first course containing any of the protein foods mentioned, or if you drink more than the 275ml (½ pint) of milk, or sprinkle some extra nuts and raisins over your muesli or salad, or even eat more fruit and vegetables, you will in fact be getting more than the 60g protein – and most meat-eaters do in fact eat much more protein than they need.

  You may be wondering whether the protein derived from

vegetable sources, from such foods as pulses, nuts, potatoes, greens, wholemeal bread and fruit, is as good a quality as that obtained from animals and animal products. In particular, you may wonder whether there will be a subtle something missing from your diet which will adversely affect your unborn child – or reveal itself as a weakness in future generations. The answer is that protein obtained from these vegetable sources is just as good as animal protein. Neither you nor your unborn child will lack any vital nutrient.

There are many myths concerning protein. At one time animal and vegetable proteins were divided into two categories and called first- and second-class proteins respectively. Then it was found that all protein was made up of twenty-two amino acids, the mixture and proportions of these varying in different foods. Of these amino acids, fourteen can be produced from components of other foods by a human adult, and eight cannot. These eight are known as 'essential amino acids'. Many animal foods contain these eight essential amino acids in roughly the right proportions for the body to use easily, though some, such as gelatine, are seriously unbalanced. The eight essential amino acids are also found in non-animal foods, but generally not in proportions which are as convenient for the body. Lentils, for instance, are rich in the amino acids isoleucine and lysine. In order to be able to use these, the body needs to be able to mix them with the amino acids tryptophan and methionine. But although lentils contain some tryptophan and methionine, they do not contain enough to marry up with all the isoleucine and lysine, so some of these amino acids are wasted.

The same is true of cereals, nuts and seeds, except that here the amino acids are the other way round: this group is rich in tryptophan and methionine and weak in isoleucine and lysine. (It's worth remembering, incidentally, that no animal protein, with the exception of human breast milk, has perfect proportions either; only about 70–75 per cent of the protein in beef and cow's milk is fully usable, and similar percentages are found in some vegetables and cereals such as potatoes, soya and oatmeal.)

In actual fact, most people eat protein from more than one

source at any meal. This means that the different essential amino acids are being supplied by a number of foods, and a deficiency of an amino acid in one food is very likely to be balanced without difficulty by an abundance in another. So, for instance, if you eat a mixture of vegetable proteins, such as beans and cereals, as in lentil soup with a roll, or baked beans on toast; or nuts and cereals, as in a rice pilaf with vegetables and toasted almonds, or breakfast muesli made from oats and nuts; or if you include a little milk or cheese with your vegetables and cereals, you increase the value of the protein available to the body. This is important information for people on very low-protein diets, and of interest to vegetarians and vegans although getting sufficient protein is not normally a problem, as I have already shown.

In practice I have found that the simplest way to meet the protein requirement is to plan each main meal around a protein food, adding a good serving of fresh fruit or vegetables with potatoes, bread or rice as required: see example menus on pages 30–1.

Iron

Extra iron is needed during pregnancy to meet the increase in the volume of blood caused by the growing baby and placenta, and to supply the reserves in the baby's liver on which she will depend for the first six months of life. Healthy blood is also necessary to enable the body to make up quickly any loss of blood at the birth. Lack of iron may also contribute to tiredness during pregnancy, so it is very important to include plenty of iron-rich foods in your diet, especially since iron tablets are not now routinely prescribed during pregnancy.

The best sources of iron for vegetarians and vegans are given below, together with the proportion of the 15g recommended daily allowance (RDA) for pregnant women which reasonable-sized portions supply.

Food	Iron Content mg	RDA %
Dried fruit		
100g (4 oz) dried apricots	5.00	33
100g (4 oz) dates	1.61	11
100g (4 oz) dried figs	4.07	27
100g (4 oz) dried prunes	2.41	16
200ml (8 fl oz) prune juice	10.50	67
100g (4 oz) dried peaches	6.75	45
50g (2 oz) raisins	0.88	6
Dried beans and lentils		
50g (2 oz) dried butter beans	3.36	22
50g (2 oz) dry lentils	4.34	29
50g (2 oz) dried soya beans, low-fat flour	5.20	35
275ml (½ pint) soya milk (made from 20g/¾ oz soya flour)	2.60	17
150g (5 oz) tofu (a soft, white curd made from soya, which you can buy vacuum-packed from health shops and fresh from oriental shops)	1.50	10
Grains, cereals and cereal products		
25g (1 oz) All Bran	3.06	20
50g (2 oz) uncooked millet	2.34	
1 piece parkin (page 200)	1.30	9
25g (1 oz) oatmeal, muesli	1.17	8
50g (2 oz) (uncooked weight) brown rice and most other grains (average)	1.74	12
2 slices (50g/2 oz) wholewheat bread	1.64	11
1 rounded tablespoon wheat germ	2.00	13
Nuts and seeds		
50g (2 oz) almonds	2.40	16
50g (2 oz) cashews, brazils (approx.)	2.00	13
50g (2 oz) fresh coconut	1.18	8

25g (1 oz) pumpkin seeds	3.40	23
25g (1 oz) sunflower seeds	2.06	14

Fresh fruit and vegetables

100g (4 oz) avocado	1.50	10
1 banana (200g/7½ oz)	0.50	3
25g (1 oz) parsley	2.27	15
200g (7½ oz) baked potato, including skin	1.80	12
50g (2 oz) raw spinach	1.70	11
1 tablespoon tomato purée	1.00	7
200g (7½ oz) cooked vegetables (average)	1.00	7

Other sources

1 rounded tablespoon curry powder	15.00	100
1 large egg	1.44	10
25g (1 oz) molasses and black treacle	2.60	17
25g (1 oz) unrefined dark barbados sugar	2.25	15
2 teaspoons brewer's yeast powder	2.00	13
25g (1 oz) carob powder	1.00	7

Not all the iron in these foods can be used by the body because of the presence of other substances which prevent it being absorbed. This is true of the iron in curry powder, for instance, which comes from the iron utensils used when it is made, and although curry powder looks like an amazing source of iron, it is not known how much of this iron is available to the body. The RDA is set high to make allowance for this, but since it is mainly the non-meat sources of iron which suffer from this binding effect, it is perhaps a good idea for vegetarians and vegans to err on the generous side when planning an iron-rich diet. It's worth remembering, too, that this binding effect is lessened if the iron-containing foods are eaten with foods containing vitamin C, such as orange juice.

Unless you particularly wish to do so, it's not necessary to add up your daily iron intake. But you do need to be aware of the foods which are rich in iron and make a point of including them in your diet each day in order to reach the recommended level. Here are two examples of how it can be done:

Food	Iron Content mg	RDA %
50g (2 oz) dried soya beans, low-fat flour	5.20	35
250ml (9 fl oz) prune juice	10.50	70
	15.70	105
banana-yeast drink (page 109)	2.50	17
50g (2 oz) lentils (dried weight)	4.34	29
2 slices (50g/2 oz) wholewheat bread	1.64	11
50g (2 oz) almonds	2.40	16
50g (2 oz) uncooked millet (dried weight)	2.34	16
200g (7½ oz) baked potato	1.80	12
450g (1 lb) vegetables	2.00	13
	17.02	114

Many authorities on healthy eating suggest that it's a good idea to have a tablespoon of molasses, wheat germ and brewer's yeast each day as a dietary supplement when you're pregnant or preparing for pregnancy. If you can manage to take these supplements each day you go a long way towards meeting your iron, calcium and vitamin B requirements. One quite palatable way of taking the molasses and wheat germ (as well as some other valuable nutrients) is in the form of 'sweets': a batch of carob fudge, for instance (page 204), supplies 9.80mg iron or 65 per cent of the RDA. Or you could sprinkle wheat germ on breakfast cereal, fruit salads, on top of *au gratin* dishes, or use it to coat rissoles, and take the molasses as a drink, dissolved in hot water or milk. Some people enjoy this, but I personally do not. In my opinion, a pleasanter way to take a large dose of iron is by drinking some prune juice, which is much nicer than it sounds. You can buy it from health shops and drink it neat or take it over the course of the day, diluted with soda or sparkling water, rather as you might dilute orange squash. Alternatively, you can make an excellent iron-rich fruit salad by soaking dried peaches (from health shops) or prunes in prune juice, or you can moisten breakfast muesli with prune juice.

The need for iron is something which I have borne in mind when compiling the recipe section of this book and many of the dishes are rich in this mineral.

Calcium

Calcium is needed for the formation and health of bones and teeth, as well as other tissues. Extra calcium is needed during pregnancy for the formation of a healthy baby and your body is also creating stores in preparation for milk production. You should take care to include calcium-rich foods in your diet. The baby will take what she needs first, so if you go short you will suffer: the old saying that you lose a tooth for every baby probably has some truth in it! The only time in my life when I have had to have a lot of fillings in my teeth was after I had had my first two babies in quick succession without visiting the dentist in between.

The RDA of calcium for a pregnant woman is 1200mg and foods which are rich in calcium are as follows:

Food	Calcium mg
Milk products	
50g (2 oz) Cheddar cheese	460
150g (5 oz) natural yoghurt	230
275ml (½ pint) skim milk	350
25g (1 oz) skim milk powder	359
Soya products	
50g (2 oz) dried soya beans, low-fat flour	137

50g (2 oz) vegan cheese (page 133)   77
275ml (½ pint) vegan milk
  (unless fortified with extra calcium)   46
150g (5 oz) vegan yoghurt   23
150g (5 oz) tofu   187

Nuts and seeds
50g (2 oz) almonds, brazils, hazels (approx.)   170
50g (2 oz) walnuts (approx.)   80
25g (1 oz) sesame seeds, sesame cream (tahini),
  sunflower seeds (approx.)   135

Dried fruit
100g (4 oz) dried apricots   92
100g (4 oz) figs   284
100g (4 oz) dried peaches   35

Vegetables
225g (8 oz) cooked broccoli   360
100g (4 oz) raw cabbage   82
100g (4 oz) raw carrot   54
25g (1 oz) parsley   92
100g (4 oz) raw spinach   102
50g (2 oz) watercress   126

Other sources
25g (1 oz) carob powder   90
25g (1 oz) molasses   140

For a vegetarian, one of the easiest ways of reaching the total would be to have a daily pint of milk (which can of course be taken during the day with cereals, in drinks, and so on), or half a pint fortified with dried milk powder (page 110), which makes quite a pleasant drink, much nicer than plain milk; or half a pint of milk and 300ml (10 fl oz) natural yoghurt, and 50g (2 oz) cheese. If you're a vegan, you need to work harder to achieve the RDA, though it is still possible. You might have, say:

100g (4 oz) raw cabbage (in a salad)	82
100g (4 oz) raw carrot (in a salad)	54
225g (8 oz) cooked broccoli	360
25g (1 oz) sesame seeds or tahini	135
50g (2 oz) almonds	170
50g (2 oz) soya flour (in soya milk)	137
50g (2 oz) soya beans	137
100g (4 oz) dried figs	284
	1359

As you will see, there are various ways of meeting the daily requirement. In practice, a vegetarian would probably do so from a mixture of plant and dairy sources, rather than just from dairy produce, as in the rather extreme example given. The important thing is to become aware of the best sources of calcium for you – which means the foods you like eating – and try and include these frequently. If you can manage to take the molasses supplement each day (see page 20), that will give you a tenth of your calcium requirement.

It's surprising how much you can increase your calcium intake by small garnishes and nibbles: 15g (½ oz) parsley scattered over a meal adds 47mg calcium, 15g (½ oz) sesame seeds is 77mg, 15g (½ oz) grated cheese, 115mg. If, however, you still find this difficult, you can get a non-organic calcium called dolomite from health shops, and you could take this, stirred into fruit juices to make up your total.

B vitamins

There are thirteen B vitamins and these are grouped together because they're interdependent. They tend to occur together in the

same foods and, with the exception of B_{12}, you shouldn't take a
supplement of an individual B vitamin as this can upset the delicate
balance. The best natural source of B vitamins (except B_{12}) is
brewer's yeast powder (which is not the same thing as baking
yeast). If you can manage to eat one tablespoon or two slightly
rounded teaspoons of brewer's yeast powder (which amounts to
the same quantity but just sounds and looks less!) a day, you will
go a long way towards meeting your requirement of B vitamins,
as well as getting another 3.5mg iron. Some people like brewer's
yeast and the various brands taste different, so it's worth
experimenting until you find the one which is least unpleasant. I
must admit that I don't like the stuff, though I've found that
Barbara Griggs's banana drink (page 109) is the most palatable way
of taking it. This drink also has the advantage of supplying extra
calcium and some useful B_6 and folic acid from the banana. Other
ways of taking brewer's yeast are sprinkled over breakfast cereal,
stirred into fruit juice, or mixed with water to the consistency of
peanut butter and probably washed down with plenty more water.
If you cannot manage any of these, you can take brewer's yeast in
the form of tablets, but you probably won't be able to take so much
this way.

The best vegetarian sources of the main B vitamins are as
follows:

Vitamin B_1 (thiamine)
Thiamine is necessary for the steady release of energy from food;
some thiamine is lost when food is cooked. Best sources are:
brewer's yeast, wheat germ, brazil nuts, sunflower seeds, soya
beans and flour, fresh peanuts, oatmeal, wholewheat bread,
avocado, dried figs, prunes and raisins, sprouted lentils and alfalfa
seeds, oranges; vegetables, especially leeks, cauliflower, broccoli,
peas, parsnips, parsley, spinach, sweetcorn, baked potatoes, if you
eat the skins.

Vitamin B_2 (riboflavin)
This is essential for the utilization of energy from food. Brewer's

yeast and yeast extracts are the richest source of this vitamin for vegetarians; other good sources (for those eating dairy produce) are cheese, eggs and milk. One-third of the average intake in Britain is derived from milk, but riboflavin is destroyed by ultraviolet light, so don't leave milk standing too long on the doorstep. If you don't eat dairy produce, you need to make a special effort to include in your diet yeast and other foods containing riboflavin: almonds and hazel nuts, mushrooms, broccoli, spinach, sprouted lentils and beans, and enriched breakfast cereals. Wholewheat bread and oats, also avocado, peanuts and walnuts, are moderately good sources.

Vitamin B_3 (nicotinic acid, known as niacin in the USA)
Another B vitamin involved in the utilization of energy. It is found in brewer's yeast; wheat germ; peanuts, almonds, sesame, sunflower and pumpkin seeds, also pulses; brazil, cashew and hazel nuts; dried dates, apricots and prunes; mushrooms, peas, potato, parsley, swede, parsnip and avocado; whole-grain cereals and bread, also fortified breakfast cereals such as All Bran and Weetabix.

Vitamin B_6 (pyridoxine)
Necessary for the metabolization of amino acids and the formation of haemoglobin. Best sources for vegetarians are brewer's yeast; wholewheat bread and whole grains, also fortified breakfast cereals such as All Bran and Weetabix; wheat germ; sprouted beans and lentils; eggs and milk, including skim milk powder; sunflower seeds, walnuts, peanuts, hazel and brazil nuts; dried fruit, especially prunes and figs; raw fruit and vegetables, especially avocado, banana, swede, parsley, leeks, spinach, tomatoes, cabbage, carrots, also canned pineapple and pineapple juice.

Folic acid
Folic acid is particularly important because it is essential for the formation of DNA and RNA (the hereditary material of all organisms), and you need four times as much as usual during

pregnancy. All foods except fats, sugar and spirits contain some folic acid, but the richest source for vegetarians is brewer's yeast and yeast extracts. Vegetables, especially spinach, parsley, beetroot, broccoli, watercress and lettuce, are all good sources of folic acid. But folic acid is sensitive to heat and light and 50–90 per cent of the folic acid in vegetables can be destroyed by cooking, so if you like salads enough to eat a reasonable amount, it is better to eat these vegetables raw, or stir-fried for the shortest time possible. If, on the other hand, you don't like salads very much, you would do better to cook them so that you eat a reasonable quantity, but do try to cook them briefly in as little water as possible, and save the water for use in soups, sauces, etc. Other good sources of folic acid are cauliflower, cabbage, lettuce, tomatoes, mushrooms, orange juice and dried figs; also walnuts, peanuts, pumpkin seeds, almonds, wholemeal bread, wheat germ, oats, brown rice, bulgur wheat and other whole grains. Also useful, though not such rich sources, are oranges, carrots, bananas, cucumber, potatoes, cheese and dates.

Biotin and pantothenic acid
Deficiencies of either of these are unlikely as so little biotin is needed (and can probably be made by bacteria in the large intestine), and pantothenic acid is so widespread in food – cereals and pulses being particularly good sources.

B_{12}
The major source of B_{12} for most people is meat and dairy produce; B_{12} is almost entirely absent from plants. Some brewer's yeast is fortified with B_{12}, as are yeast extracts Barmene and, to a lesser degree, Marmite. But vegans who are not getting adequate amounts from these sources would be well advised to take a B_{12} supplement. Vegetarians can get some B_{12} from eggs and dairy produce, although I think that a B_{12} tablet in addition, two or three times a week, is a good idea whether you are pregnant or not.

Vitamin D

The body needs vitamin D in order to use calcium efficiently, and this is especially so during pregnancy. Best sources of vitamin D are cod-liver oil, which is obviously unsuitable for both vegetarians and vegans, eggs, and vitamin-D-fortified margarine, evaporated milk and skim milk powder. Vitamin D is also formed by the action of sunlight on the skin, but unless you live in a very sunny part of the world and do a lot of sunbathing, it's a wise precaution to take a vitamin D supplement. Check whether this is included in any general vitamin pills you may be given by the doctor; if it isn't, you can get one from your health shop or chemist. Be careful to measure the dose precisely as too much vitamin D is toxic.

Zinc

Zinc is a trace element which is vitally important in the formation of DNA and RNA. Again, you should make a point of including in your diet foods which are rich in this mineral. The richest sources for vegetarians are wheat germ and bran; other good sources are almonds, brazil nuts, cashews, hazel nuts, peanuts and walnuts; lentil and bean sprouts; oatmeal, brown rice, cheese, cocoa, sweetcorn, peas, milk, and fresh mango if you're feeling extravagant. Wholemeal bread and pulses are quite good sources, though the phytic acid in these may prevent some zinc absorption: the effect of this is less in well-leavened bread. A shortage of zinc often manifests itself as white flecks on the fingernails, and skin problems such as eczema and acne.

Magnesium

This is another vitally important trace element. Nuts, pulses and whole grains appear to be rich in magnesium, but again the phytic acid which is also present in these is known to interfere in their absorption to some degree, though how much is not certain. Best sources are wheat germ, wheat bran, All Bran, soya beans and flour, sprouted pulses, oatmeal, almonds, brazil nuts, cashew nuts, hazel nuts and walnuts. Dried figs, dates, peaches and apricots are also good sources, as is well-leavened wholewheat bread. Potatoes, bananas, and fresh fruit and vegetables generally, also contribute.

Iodine

Iodine is necessary for the proper functioning of the thyroid gland. The main sources are seafoods (including seaweeds and thus vegetarian jelling agents such as agar-agar and gelozone) and iodized table salt. For vegetarians and vegans, a good way of making sure you're getting enough iodine is to add a pinch of kelp powder (from health shops) to food two or three times a week, or to take kelp tablets regularly. (Kelp is a type of seaweed.)

Creating a balanced diet

Now you've read this far you may well be feeling quite confused by all the dietary requirements and the various possible sources. It does seem complicated: yet it's perhaps comforting to remember that most people in this country manage to keep reasonably fit and to produce healthy babies without knowing much at all about nutrition! Yet there is little doubt that by building your diet around the vitamin- and mineral-rich foods you can improve your own health and give the best possible start for your baby. Here is a suggested plan of action.

If you're improving your health in preparation for becoming pregnant in the future, I would strongly advise you to rely on some form of contraception other than the pill. The pill is known to affect the body's ability to metabolize vitamin B_6, B_2, B_{12} and folic acid, also zinc, copper and iron. If you are unsure about your general state of health, or have had a miscarriage or difficult previous pregnancy, you might consider visiting one of the Foresight clinics: see page 213 for further information.

Try to take the daily dietary supplements of 1 tablespoon each of brewer's yeast (or some yeast tablets), molasses and wheat germ, as suggested on page 20, to give you a good iron/calcium/vitamin B basis to the day. Alternatively, if you think your diet has been lacking some nutrients, consider taking a multivitamin pill each day for a time, to give yourself a boost while you improve your diet.

Consider taking a B_{12} and vitamin D supplement, and kelp for iodine (unless these are included in any multivitamin pill you're taking).

Some foods crop up time and again in the lists of sources of nutrients. Concentrate especially on these and include them in your meals and nibbles as often as possible. They are:

brewer's yeast and yeast extracts
dried fruits, especially figs, also prunes and prune juice, apricots, peaches and dates
cereals, especially wheat germ, also wholewheat bread, and the whole-grain cereals such as oats, buckwheat, bulgur wheat, brown rice and millet; also All Bran and fortified wholewheat breakfast cereals
pulses, especially soya, soya flour, and sprouted pulses such as lentils, mung beans and chickpeas
nuts and seeds, especially almonds, hazel nuts, cashew nuts, walnuts, brazil nuts, peanuts, sunflower, sesame and pumpkin seeds
fresh fruit and vegetables, especially raw spinach, parsley, watercress, lettuce, broccoli (cooked and raw), raw cabbage, carrots, swede, cauliflower and mushrooms; avocado, bananas and oranges
molasses

Menu-building

It's not difficult to build meals from these basic foods. Here are some ideas; the dishes mentioned can be found in the recipe section.

Breakfast

TO START

Natural yoghurt with wheat germ and chopped banana or dried figs or dates and a sprinkling of chopped walnuts, almonds or brazil nuts

Whole-grain muesli mixed with extra wheat germ and chopped figs, dates or other dried fruit, with dairy (preferably skim) milk, soya or nut milk (nuts in water liquidized to make a milk), with extra chopped nuts, as above

Prunes, apricots, peaches or figs soaked overnight in prune juice and served with natural yoghurt (or vegan yoghurt) and some grated or chopped brazil nuts, almonds or walnuts

All Bran or other enriched wholewheat cereal with chopped figs or other dried fruit and some chopped nuts, with skim milk or soya milk

Chopped fresh fruit, perhaps with grated nuts and/or raisins, also yoghurt, if liked

TO FOLLOW

Wholemeal toast as required, spread with yeast extract if liked

Orange juice, tea, herb tea, coffee or a coffee substitute to drink (best to reduce coffee intake if possible, as this can interfere with absorption of some vitamins)

FOR A COOKED BREAKFAST

Mushrooms on wholewheat toast

Baked beans on wholewheat toast

Boiled, poached or scrambled egg or an omelette

Lunch

Try and make this a salad-based meal if possible, perhaps with a warming soup or cup of yeast extract or miso (a tasty, nutritious paste made from fermented soya beans) in hot water when the weather is cold. Here are some suggestions.

Vitality salad bowl, perhaps with wholewheat pitta bread. For
pudding: orange, banana, special molasses sweets or soaked
prunes, peaches or apricots, or chopped figs in natural yoghurt
or vegan yoghurt

Tabbouleh, sliced tomatoes; pudding as above

Avocado, mushroom and walnut salad, with some watercress and
wholewheat bread; pudding, if required, as above

Grated swede salad, wholewheat bread and nut spread or a soya
sausage or sprouted pulses; pudding as above

Wholewheat sandwich: wholewheat bread, yeast extract or nut
spread with lots of salad filling; apple, banana or orange, or one
of the nutritious 'sweets'

Main course cabbage salad and a baked potato, with cottage cheese
or grated cheese if liked; pudding as above

Evening meal

Buckwheat bake, spinach salad; baked apples with dried fruit and
single cream or tofu topping

Butter bean and vegetable casserole, baked potato or cooked
brown rice or millet, watercress; apricot fool

Chunky nut and vegetable roast, baked potato, main course
cabbage salad; muesli (oaty version)

Leek and potato pie, cooked broccoli; dried fruit compote

Brown rice with tomatoes and walnuts, spinach salad or
watercress; yoghurt, banana and crunchy granola

Pasta with lentil and red pepper sauce, green salad; apples and
dried fruit with cream or tofu topping

Tofu fritters with lemon, yoghurt and parsley sauce, green salad,
sliced tomatoes; apricots with nut cream

If you plan your meals along these lines you should enjoy
delicious and varied meals and have no worries about being
undernourished.

Morning sickness, food cravings and foods to be avoided

When you first become pregnant you may well feel slightly sick and not much like eating. During these early days you may find that there are only certain things you fancy having. Some people find milk, milky drinks and yoghurt helpful, others find they turn to fresh fruits, salads or wholemeal bread. Herb teas, especially peppermint, lime, chamomile and meadowsweet (see page 113), can be useful.

For most people this faddy, sick stage only lasts for the first few weeks. If you do find you cannot eat normally, don't be anxious and feel that your baby is being undernourished. You only need to worry if you are sick the whole time and cannot keep anything down. In this case, the baby could be at risk, and you should see your doctor. Otherwise, just try to see that the foods you do eat are as whole and natural as possible.

Once you know what is happening, you will probably find that you can control the nausea to some extent by having something to eat or drink as soon as you feel that strange, hungry, sick feeling. It is often helpful to avoid fatty foods and to eat little and often. Wholemeal biscuits might be helpful, as might dates or a drink of apple or orange juice.

The tendency to have odd cravings for foods in pregnancy is well known and, within reason, these do not usually do any harm and pass as pregnancy progresses. Medical opinion now suggests that alcohol is best avoided during pregnancy and warns seriously against smoking. Both of these can be harmful to the baby. Smoking is associated with low birth weight and unlike most things it has a worse effect later in pregnancy than in the first few weeks. So it's never too late to cut down or give up smoking.

Similarly, pills of any kind should be regarded with suspicion and certainly only taken when prescribed by a doctor in the knowledge of your pregnancy.

Heartburn and constipation

Two problems which are very common in pregnancy, because of the extra pressure put on the digestive system by the growing baby, are heartburn and constipation. Both conditions can be helped by your diet.

If you are suffering from heartburn it may help to ease the condition if you eat frequent small meals and cut out fatty foods as much as possible. It can also be very helpful to avoid eating concentrated starches (potatoes, bread, brown rice and other cereals) with concentrated protein (cheese, eggs, dairy products). Plan for a starch meal, which can include nuts and seeds and all the fresh vegetables you want, plus the 'starchy' fruits (dates, dried fruit, bananas and very sweet grapes); and a protein meal, which should be based on protein, including nuts and seeds and all kinds of vegetables (except potatoes) and fruits (except the starchy ones mentioned above – raisins are all right). Pulses, being a half-and-half protein-carbohydrate mix, unfortunately do not fit into this scheme – unless they're sprouted first, when they can be treated as vegetables.

A tendency towards constipation can be helped by the inclusion in your diet of foods which are high in fibre. Wholemeal bread (which can be eaten without butter if you need to watch the calories), bran to stir into your breakfast cereal, soup or yoghurt, and bran products are all high in fibre, as are pulses, nuts, fresh vegetables, including potatoes, and fruits, especially raspberries. If, in addition to constipation, you're also suffering from piles, try to include buckwheat in your diet as often as possible, since this contains rutin which is a natural remedy for piles, as well as for varicose veins.

Weight control during pregnancy

During your pregnancy a close check will be kept on your weight. There is no reason why a vegetarian diet should be any more fattening that a conventional one, but pregnancy is a time when many women, myself included, find they gain extra pounds very easily. If you find that your weight is increasing too rapidly, you would be wise to concentrate on the low-calorie protein foods such as cottage and curd cheese, yoghurt, cheese, bean curd (tofu), pulses, wheat germ and skim milk, with liberal amounts of fresh vegetables and fruit.

Some people are now questioning, however, the wisdom of restricting weight gain too drastically during pregnancy. I rather go along with this view. Some reserves of fat (but not too many!) are helpful when it comes to breast-feeding and helping you to weather the general stresses and strains of the early days with a young baby. And if you breast-feed for at least six months, you will almost certainly find that this extra weight just rolls away even though you are, quite rightly, eating more than normal during breast-feeding. But you do have to be patient while the food stores, in the form of your fat, are gradually used up in the production of milk for the baby. Then, with any luck, you'll find you're thinner and more gorgeous than ever. But if not, then that is the time to restrict your calories to between 1200 or 1500 a day (as against 2750 when breast-feeding) and get back your slim figure.

Nutritional values of foods throughout this chapter are taken from R. A. McCance and E. M. Widdowson, *The Composition of Foods*, and *Nutrition Almanac* (Nutrition Search Inc.).

2 Pregnancy and Preparations for the Birth

Choosing the place of birth

Once your pregnancy has been confirmed, you will need to decide where you would like the birth to take place and, if it's in hospital, the length of time that you'll stay. If it's your first baby, or if you are considered to be in any way 'at risk' because of previous difficulties, low blood count, poor home conditions or age, you will probably be wise to go to hospital. But if there is more than one hospital taking admittances from your area it is certainly worth finding out all you can about each one. Contact your local National Childbirth Trust (NCT) group (see page 213) and ask about the experiences of other mothers. Hospitals vary in their approach, and by asking around you are more likely to find the one which will give you the kind of birth conditions you would like. Some hospitals are more orientated towards natural childbirth than others and will be more sympathetic towards the use of breathing exercises during labour (see pages 46–7), requests for the minimum of painkilling drugs and use of birth positions other than lying on your back. The work of doctors Frederick Leboyer and Michel Odent have had a considerable impact, and some hospitals will let you have a Leboyer- or Odent-style delivery, if you ask for this. Similarly, some hospitals are more helpful than others when it comes to starting breast-feeding and, again, it is worthwhile talking to those who have recently given birth to find out how they fared at a particular hospital. Make a point of asking whether they were allowed to have the baby in their room with them all the time.

This arrangement, known as 'rooming-in', is so helpful in establishing breast-feeding, as explained on pages 54–7.

Another possibility in some areas is the GP Unit, which is a fully equipped maternity unit where you can have your baby delivered by your own doctor and the midwife who has been looking after you at the antenatal sessions, rather than by doctors and nurses you don't know. A further option in some areas is the Domino System (meaning Domiciliary-In-Out) where your midwife cares for you antenatally, takes you into hospital when you are in labour, delivers you and brings you home a few hours later to care for you at home. Some people value this familiarity and feeling of continuity. Should there be any complications in your pregnancy, however, you will probably be asked to have the baby in hospital in the usual way instead.

If you opt for a hospital or GP Unit, you will probably be given the choice of a 48-hour stay or longer. If you choose the shorter stay, a local midwife will visit you in your own home for ten days afterwards to attend to your needs and those of the baby. She will show you how to bath the baby and advise you about breast-feeding. The advantage of the short stay is that you get back into the peace and familiarity of your home sooner, but you will need either the active support of a competent, caring and practical partner, or of a sensitive, non-aggravating relative or friend who can stay with you for a week or so. It's often so much easier to establish the breast-feeding routine at home when you and the baby have the time and peace to learn about each other quietly, away from the hustle and strangeness of hospital.

The final possibility is to opt for a home delivery. Since the Peel report of 1970 it has become government policy to provide sufficient hospital facilities for every confinement and the number of home deliveries has declined steadily. However, the Midwives acts of 1936 and 1951, which make it compulsory for local authorities to supply sufficient midwives for all births in their area, are still in force. If called to attend a birth a midwife is obliged to do so. You do still therefore have the right to have your baby at home if you choose to do so. The first step towards achieving this is to talk the matter over with your GP and find out whether he is willing and able to assist you, or, failing that, whether there is another doctor in the practice who can. It is best to have this discussion with your GP when you first have your pregnancy confirmed, before you sign the form asking your GP to provide maternity care. If your own GP is unwilling for you to have a home delivery, you have the right to transfer to another doctor for the period of your antenatal care, birth and the postnatal period, but it is more difficult to do this if you have already signed the form. Your nearest NCT group may have a list of local doctors who are sympathetic towards home confinement, and you might also find it helpful to contact The Society for the Support of Home Confinement (see page 213 for address).

If you really want a home confinement, your home conditions are suitable and there are no complications which would put you 'at risk', there is no reason why you should not have one. Read the books listed on page 214 for full information on having your baby at home and much useful advice.

Antenatal care

It goes without saying that you will regularly attend the antenatal clinic either at your doctor's surgery or the hospital. During the course of this antenatal care, you may be offered certain tests to check on the baby's growth and to spot any genetic abnormality. So many tests are now available that it is outside the scope of this book to cover them all. However, I would just like to comment briefly on two of the most common ones: ultrasound and amniocentesis. Fuller descriptions of these tests and others are given by Sally Inch in her book *Birthrights* (see Further Reading, page 214).

An ultrasound scan is now sometimes given routinely in the sixteenth week of pregnancy. This is ostensibly to check on the baby's progress – especially if there is some question over dates – and of course it also gives you the thrill of seeing your baby.

However, I would question the validity and wisdom of performing these scans so freely, and I personally would refuse to have one unless there was a real medical reason for doing one. As yet there is no long-term research to show that scans are harmless (some possible problems, e.g., some cancers, have a latency period of between fifteen and thirty years), although, equally, there is no evidence that they are not.

Amniocentesis is another test which you may be offered if you are in a 'high-risk' category for Down's syndrome. The test carries with it an increased possibility of miscarriage (although this risk is declining), and other slight risks to the baby. However, a new test is being introduced in which some cells are taken from the cervix, avoiding the dangers mentioned. At the time of writing, as far as I know, this test is not yet available. These tests do not reveal the degree of handicap and there are sometimes false positives which may cause great anxiety. Before having either of these tests, however, it is a good idea to think about and discuss with your partner whether you would want to have an abortion if birth defects were revealed. If you know you wouldn't want an abortion in any case, is there any point in having the test done?

As medical science advances, it brings many benefits, for which one can feel nothing but gratitude. It is a pity, though, if it also causes us to lose confidence in the ability of the human body to function normally without intervention and, in particular, to produce healthy, beautiful babies, just as it has done for thousands of years. So do your best to nourish and care for your body, but have faith in it and its ability to produce a perfect baby.

Preparation for breast-feeding

Most experts now recognize that breast-feeding gives a baby the best possible start in life. Although there are some excellent dried formula milks on the market, no one has been able to make an exact replica of breast milk, with its delicate balance of nutrients and built-in immunity which passes from mother to baby. Neither can a bottle replace the closeness and skin contact which a baby gets when feeding from her mother. But apart from all this, I do think it is worth stressing how much easier and more practical breast-feeding is, once it's established, than bottle-feeding. There's no sterilizing of bottle and equipment, no buying of milk powder, no heating up of milk during the small hours of the night, no chance of forgetting the baby's food if you go out for the day. And with breast-feeding you have the means of comforting your baby immediately and as often as necessary. Also, if you're patient, it's a natural means of losing any extra pounds you've put on during pregnancy, as mentioned on page 34.

Although breast-feeding is so simple, because bottle-feeding was fashionable for such a long time not everyone is yet familiar with the rather different technique of breast-feeding. You may therefore get some confusing advice as you, and the baby, try to learn how to do it. It is therefore a good idea to prepare yourself before the birth by reading some of the very good books that are now available. I've mentioned my own favourites on page 215. No other special preparations are necessary apart from this reading, and maintaining a good diet. Just wash your breasts as usual when you bath or shower, but don't use soap which can wash away the natural secretions that protect against soreness when the baby starts to suck. When you do wash your breasts, it's a good idea to get used to handling them so that you don't feel awkward and embarrassed about this when the time comes to start breast-feeding.

Nursing bras and clothes for breast-feeding

Tender and enlarged breasts may be one of the first signs that you're pregnant, and your breasts will continue to expand during your pregnancy so that you will need at least one set of new bras, probably more. Breast-feeding should not spoil the shape of your breasts but if you normally wear a bra for comfort and support you will certainly want to wear a properly supportive one during pregnancy and while you're breast-feeding. You'd probably be more comfortable wearing one at night as well as during the day, so it's worth finding one that feels right. The NCT sells an excellent maternity bra called Mava, which can be fitted at about five months and should see you through the rest of your pregnancy and the early weeks of breast-feeding. (As breast-feeding progresses, you will find that your breasts shrink and you can progress backwards through your pregnancy bras until you get back to your normal size again.) Cotton bras are more practical than nylon as they let the skin breathe and thus help to prevent sore nipples. I must add that in order to do their job effectively good maternity bras, such as the Mava previously mentioned, do tend to look a little more substantial than those you may have been used to. Don't let this put you off; a good maternity bra will be much more comfortable and supportive than a flimsy one. Look for a bra which has front flaps that unhook, or cups which open individually, for easy feeding.

Clothes for wearing after the birth should be as easy to wash as your baby's clothes: the early days of breast-feeding can be messy, and babies frequently 'burp' up small quantities of milk after feeding. So have easy-care clothes which allow you to feed and handle your baby without worrying about the odd splash and stain. Cotton T-shirts, or jumpers which you can pull up for feeding, or shirts, dresses and blouses which button down the front, are the most practical. You will also need some decent nighties for wearing in hospital and for the days after the birth. If you're buying new ones, and if the budget allows, cosy, long-sleeved, Victorian-style ones, which open down the front, are pretty and practical for chilly night-feeds. A big, pretty, colourful shawl which you can pop round your shoulders during the night, or use to wrap around yourself and the baby for privacy when you're breast-feeding in a public place, is also most useful. This would be a lovely present for a mum-to-be.

However careful you have been during your pregnancy, you will probably find, as most of us do, that you cannot get into any of your old clothes – except for your maternity ones, of which you are heartily sick – immediately after you have had the baby. So if you can manage it, consider buying yourself one or two really pretty, easy-to-wash, front-opening, new dresses, or jumpers and skirts, a size or two larger than usual. These will be a great morale-booster in the early days after the baby is born, when you may still be feeling rather fat and perhaps suffering a bit from postnatal depression.

Buying baby clothes

When choosing clothes for a young baby, bear in mind the ease with which the clothes can be used and washed. It helps, for instance, if all the clothes and bedding are machine-washable; if the clothes open down the front so that you do not have to turn the baby over, and if the armholes are of the wide, raglan type which make it easier to get the little arms through the sleeves. Avoid ribbons, strings and complicated fastenings that can easily get tangled up. Machine-washable garments made of stretch fabric, and fastening simply up the front, are the most practical. You will need enough clothes to allow for frequent washing. A basic layette would be:

3 vests, made from soft, non-irritant material and with envelope necks so that they're easy to pop over the baby's head. An alternative is the stretch body-suit, which is like a vest and pants combined with poppers at the crutch, over baby's nappy and plastic pants. This avoids the problem of a vest riding up, and is cosy for a young baby, but the trouble with these is that if the baby's nappy leaks, you have more clothes to change

3 stretch suits, or 6 of these if you're using them at night-time in place of nighties. Being made of stretch fabric, these last well, but keep a check on the feet as the months go by to make sure there's plenty of room for the baby's toes

3 nighties: these are optional and you might prefer to use stretch suits night and day. If you do buy nighties, choose ones with

wide raglan sleeves made from a soft, easy-to-wash and non-iron fabric. (When I was expecting my first baby I made some beautiful smocked vyella nighties, but these were impractical because I never had time to iron them. For my second baby I used them again but had stretch suits as well, but with my third baby I abandoned nighties in favour of stretch suits only and had a much easier time!)

3 knitted jackets: these should be machine-washable, soft-textured and without lacy holes which can trap tiny fingers. As with the nighties, choose a roomy sleeved style with snugly fitting cuffs. I found the soft, fine-knitted manufactured ones washed and wore better than the hand-knitted ones. But whichever type you decide on, don't get them too soon as you'll probably be given some

2 or 3 pairs of bootees to wear with the nightgowns

a woolly bonnet, and perhaps 2 pairs of mitts – make sure there aren't any lengths of wool inside the mitts to entangle baby's fingers. Stretch suits usually have turn-back mitten cuffs which are fine for a tiny baby

2 lightweight cotton shawls for wrapping the new baby securely when putting her into the cot (see page 64)

2 dozen terry-towelling nappies and a packet of nappy pins, unless you're planning to use disposables

8–12 one-way nappies (again, unless you're planning to use disposables). These are optional, but help to keep the baby more comfortable. They're rectangles of a special fabric which lets water through but not back again. Placed inside a normal fabric or disposable nappy, they will help to keep baby's bottom dry. These nappies are thin and dry quickly after washing

3 pairs of plastic pants, if you're using fabric nappies. The easiest to use with a young baby (and the cheapest) are probably the ones which tie up at the baby's hips. These are also a little more porous than the other kinds, which helps to avoid nappy rash

Disposable nappies, if you are intending to use these, and special plastic pants to go with them. The easiest (and most expensive) disposable nappies to use on a young baby are the ones which

come complete with plastic outer layer and simply stick in place.
Don't get too many of any one type until you have tried them
to find which sort you prefer
2 cotton cellular blankets for the cot
2 cot sheets, made from flannellette, or fitted stretch type

This sounds quite a daunting list and certainly isn't cheap.
However, you may well be given some of the items by kind friends
and relations. Since tiny babies grow out of their first clothes
before they're anything like worn out, many mothers are only too
pleased to be able to pass these on. Your local NCT could be a good
source of such second-hand baby clothes.

General equipment

Very good bargains can often be found by looking in the personal
columns of local newspapers, or through your NCT branch.
Equipment bought in this way should be carefully checked for
safety, and can be cleaned by washing with soap and water then
rinsing and wiping over with feeding-bottle sterilizer diluted in
water. Make sure when buying second-hand equipment that it still
conforms to safety regulations.

Cots, prams and pushchairs
You'll want to be able to move the cot around the house so that
the baby can be close to you. A Moses basket, cot-on-wheels or
carry cot is therefore the most practical. If you buy a carry cot on
a transporter, remember that this is not really meant for a lot of
outdoor use; even if it has a hood, the insulation and the springing
may not be adequate for the baby's safety and comfort. Make sure
that the transporter or stand is safe and untippable, with a rail all
round to stop the cot from slipping.

Some people put their baby straight into a big cot and this can
save money. But it's difficult to make a tiny baby really cosy in –
what appears to her to be – a vast cot; and of course you cannot
move a big cot around, which is inconvenient and cuts baby off

from the warmth and noise of family life.

The type of pram you buy depends on your lifestyle. A sturdy, coach-built pram is ideal if you can afford it, have somewhere to store it, and if you do a fair amount of walking. This kind of pram provides a comfortable and safe place for baby to sleep outside, and really comes into its own if and when you have a toddler in tow as well, because the toddler can sit on the pram in a toddler seat. You can buy a rack to fit underneath the pram and this is useful for shopping. If you mainly use the car to get around, a fold-up pram might be a better buy. Make sure that this is properly insulated and sprung. Whichever type of pram you choose, check that there are rings for attaching a safety harness when the baby is older. I also consider a cat-net to be an essential. Cats like nothing better than to curl up on top of a warm baby and they can cause suffocation. Your baby will be an atttraction to the neighbouring cats even if you haven't one of your own.

Pushchairs come in many varieties and again it is a question of finding the right one for your lifestyle. Some of the reclining or convertible pushchairs can be used for tiny babies, but again check the insulation, and use with a special, padded, pushchair bag or extra blankets underneath the baby if necessary. The 'stroller' type pushchairs which fold up like an umbrella are extremely useful. I think it is a pity most of these are designed with the handles behind the baby; it is nicer for both baby and mother if they can see each other and communicate as they walk along.

Slings and carriers

A baby sling or carrier enables you to keep your baby close to you while leaving your hands free and can therefore be most useful, especially if you have a lively, non-sleeping baby who wants to see what you're doing almost from birth. For use in the home, and for young babies, the soft, fabric type of sling that you tie around you with straps is best. Choose one with a head support and make sure that baby's legs, which are outside the sling, do not get cold. For use outside, and for carrying an older baby, a metal-framed carrier which you wear on your back is better. Again, watch baby's legs for warmth. Although I think these slings and carriers are an excellent idea, and some mums manage them well, I wasn't too successful with them. My babies tended to be robust and lively and I felt dragged down by their weight. I think they're a great way for dad to carry the baby, though!

Chairs and high chairs

You won't need a high chair until the baby can sit up, but it is useful to have a chair which you can put a tiny baby in so that she can lie propped up but well supported and see what is going on. This, in my opinion, is an essential – again – if you happen to have a lively baby who prefers looking to sleeping, even from her earliest days! A little rocking cradle chair, consisting of a piece of material supported on a metal frame, is light and quite inexpensive. Alternatively, you can buy a convertible moulded plastic chair which can be used first in a tipped-back position for a tiny baby and then in a sitting-up position by an older baby. Either of these are well worth having and will make the early baby days easier.

Nappy-changing and washing equipment

A plastic-covered, padded, nappy-changing mat may sound like a luxury and I would not have thought of buying one for myself. But I shall always be grateful to the kind friend who gave me one when my first baby was born. It is in fact a most useful piece of equipment to have, providing the ideal surface for changing baby's nappy whether you're doing this on the floor, in bed, or in a chair with the changing mat over your knees. As it's waterproof, it also means that the baby can have a few minutes' 'kicking time' without a nappy as part of the nappy-changing routine.

Prepare yourself for the onslaught of dirty nappies. If you're planning to use towelling nappies, buy two lidded, polythene nappy buckets, some nappy sterilizer and soap powder (not detergent or biological powders, which can aggravate a baby's sensitive skin). A washing machine, especially an automatic one, and a means of getting things dry which does not depend on the weather really will make all the difference to your life. This is true even if you're going to use disposable nappies: babies get through an incredible quantity of clothes and bedding!

If you're going to use disposable nappies, equip yourself with one or two pedal-bins and liners for getting rid of the dirty nappies: these should never be put down the loo.

Baby bath

Strictly speaking, I think a baby bath is something you can do without. When the baby is tiny a plastic washing-up bowl is fine and because it's small the baby seems to be in less danger of slipping uncontrollably into the water. Once this has been outgrown you can use the sink, if your kitchen is warm, or the ordinary bath. This saves time and avoids the need to mess around with jugs and buckets of water. If this idea does not appeal to you, though, the little inflatable baby baths which you blow up like a paddling pool are practical, fairly inexpensive to buy and can be filled with the minimum of water.

Antenatal classes

It's worth preparing yourself for the birth by attending some antenatal classes. I highly recommend those run by the National Childbirth Trust. These give a very thorough preparation for the birth, breast-feeding and early baby care. The exercises, in particular the special relaxation and breathing techniques which they teach, are excellent.

While preparing yourself by reading, attending antenatal classes and practising breathing and relaxation, try not to get a fixed idea of how things 'ought' to go. Every labour is different, every birth a unique experience, and no one can predict beforehand exactly what will happen. Be prepared to let your labour take its course and do not feel you have 'failed' if you find you do need some help with a painkiller or gas and air – this is probably preferable to pethidine and other drugs which can make you (and the baby) unduly dopey – or if your labour does not proceed as you'd hoped, and you have to have the baby induced, delivered by forceps or Caesarean section.

The NCT headquarters (address on page 213) will give you the address of your local branch and NCT antenatal teacher, also any NCT-trained breast-feeding counsellors in your area. The NCT also has a very good postnatal support system for new mothers run on a local basis by other mothers. This is most helpful, especially if you're just giving up work to have your first baby and have few local contacts as a result. Another good way of getting to know other mums in your immediate area is to join a babysitting circle. Obviously you won't need to use this for a while, but in the meantime you can meet some of the other members of the circle, and it's reassuring to know you can get a babysitter later, when you need one.

Organizing your home

A little forethought can make all the difference to how you feel and how you cope in the early days after the birth of your baby. If this is your first baby you will probably have little idea how dramatically its arrival will affect you, your partner and your home. In the early days after the birth, the needs of the baby will fully occupy your day to the exclusion of almost everything else. If your baby is anything like the majority, you will also be coping with many interruptions during the night, and you will be coping with this having been through one of the most intense experiences of your life; birth, with its enormous demands on you, physically, mentally and emotionally.

Therefore, organize things so that your life is as easy as possible for you during the first six weeks or so after the birth. Lay in a good supply of food, especially the wholefoods which are quick and easy to prepare. Don't be ashamed of stocking up on some of the healthier convenience foods, too, such as baked beans, canned soups, beans and nut savouries, and frozen vegetables. If you have a deepfreeze, try to stock this up with ready-to-heat meals: many vegetarian dishes freeze perfectly, and some practical and nutritious one are given on pages 135–51.

Experienced mothers never turn down any offers of help with housework, washing or shopping. Having a relative or friend to stay with you or to pop in for a few hours each day for a week or so after the birth, to deal with the cleaning, washing and cooking, can make such a difference. Whether or not this is possible it's worth looking at your home from the point of view of easy cleaning. Remove any unnecessary dust-traps, like ornaments, for instance, or have an extra-long lead fitted to the vacuum cleaner so that you can whizz it over several rooms without having to unplug it.

Packing for hospital

The hospital will give you a list of things to bring in with you, and, as all the books say, you should have your case packed by the time you're seven months pregnant. It's no fun trying to gather things together between contractions in the middle of the night. When you pack, it's a good idea to include some honey and a teaspoon, or some dried fruit or homemade 'high-energy' biscuits or sweets (pages 202–5). These are comforting and reviving after the birth – one time when a quick dose of sugar for the system is both permissible and helpful, especially if you have been without food for several hours.

Once the birth is over and you have been washed, you will probably be given something to eat or at least a cup of tea, depending on the time of day. Your partner, who, if you're lucky, has been with you throughout the experience, won't be given any food and may not be able to get any, if the baby is born at an awkward time of day or night. So, if you can manage it before you leave for the hospital, it's a good idea to pack up some food, or at least to pack some non-perishable things like wholewheat biscuits and nuts and raisins: some ideas for this packed meal are given on pages 128–34. If you tell the hospital you're vegetarian when you're admitted, the hospital dietician will probably come and see you to discuss your needs and you will be given vegetarian meals.

The father's role

With so much attention focused on the mother-to-be, it is easy to overlook or underemphasize the very important part which the prospective father can play in the preparations. Some men find it difficult to become interested in the new baby when it's just a bulge; others take great delight in the whole business of pregnancy and preparations for the birth. Most antenatal classes have at least one session when prospective fathers are invited to attend and, if you're lucky, this won't clash with an important football replay, as it did when I was expecting my youngest baby.

A father-to-be who has attended the relevant clinic or antenatal visits and knows (as far as is ever possible) what to expect at the birth, and the kind of relaxation and breathing exercises which his partner is endeavouring to put into practice, can be so very helpful when the time comes. In fact, speaking from the woman's point of view, I cannot overemphasize how much it means to have the support of a caring and reasonably informed partner. Some women find it a comfort to have their backs rubbed or their brow wiped, though I personally didn't want to be touched, but even if there's apparently nothing for him to do except perhaps hold her hand, his presence and emotional support means everything.

Men who have been through this experience are deeply stirred by it; many say they never again feel quite the same, that it deepens their love and respect for their partner 'seeing what she went through', and gives them a specially close bond with their child. It is wonderful to be able to share the thrill of the first sight and sound of the baby, especially when you've been together through the agony of labour at its height.

Of course, initially, the father's role is not as glamorous – and in some ways rewarding – as the mother's. He does not have the joy of being able to breast-feed the baby (although in my opinion any possible sexual connotations here are greatly overstated); neither does he have the satisfaction of being adored and needed in quite the same way as the mother. His role at this time is more of a supportive nature; taking turns at comforting and rocking a fretful baby in the evening; taking over so that the mother can have a much-needed rest; perhaps (with luck) making a meal. A good father also needs to be forbearing; not reacting angrily when snapped at by a tense, exhausted and hormonally disorientated partner; not being jealous of the attention she is having to give the baby and, above all, helping her to feel she's doing well and that she's still attractive (which she will probably doubt).

Later on, from the time the baby is about five months and onwards, the father will be rewarded by the baby's growing interest in him. The time comes when babies want novelty, and then nothing is more delightful than this male figure who appears in the evening and makes a nice change from the 'boring' mother who has been around all day. Fathers who can exploit this, enjoying a time of play and fun, will not only (again) help their partners by taking some of the pressure off, but will increasingly build up their own special relationship with the baby. It will – quite rightly – be different from the mother's, but equally important to the health and happiness of the developing baby and the family as a whole.

3 Birth and the First Few Days

The birth

The more you and the medical staff attending the birth know about relaxation and the natural control of pain during childbirth, the easier it is to have a completely natural birth without drugs. As Sally Inch points out in her most helpful book *Birthrights*, most of the world's mothers receive few or no drugs in labour or delivery. What they have instead is constant emotional support from familiar people around them, together with the ingrained belief that chidbirth is a completely natural process and that even at its most intense the pain will not become too much for them. This is the kind of reassurance that a woman needs at the height of her labour; to be helped to hang on with her breathing and relaxation and to know that, just when she thinks she will never be able to cope any longer with the pain, it will be over, and she will have the bliss of being able to push for the second stage. If you've had a reasonably natural birth with a first baby, it is far easier to have a completely natural one for the second and subsequent babies because you have the confidence of knowing this; if you can hang on to this thought – and if those attending you could give reassurance over this, too – you are less likely to need drugs. Giving birth, for most of us, is an extremely testing experience, but it is possible to cope without drugs and painkillers if you have confidence in your ability to hang on long enough. It was undoubtedly the midwife's confidence in me that prevented me from having any drugs when my first baby was born. I thought that it was a tough birth, although I used the NCT breathing method throughout (and certainly couldn't have managed without drugs if I had not had this). Afterwards, I asked her slightly grudgingly why she hadn't given me gas and air when I felt I'd needed it. She replied that she thought I was coping so well without that it would be a pity to spoil it, and she knew I was almost through the worst at that point anyway. I am very grateful to her for this, and I hope that this attitude will become more common.

In an ideal situation, you should be handed your baby, unwrapped, immediately she has been born. This skin contact has an important part to play in the mother-child bonding process. It requires a specially heated delivery room (which most are) to prevent the wet newborn baby from cooling down too rapidly, but an increasing number of hospitals are providing the right conditions.

Provided the baby is healthy, your first cradling should not be hurried. Research has shown that the baby is especially able to interact with its parents immediately after birth and, ideally, mother and father should be allowed a quiet time to look at, talk to and love their baby immediately after she has been born. This can be a most magical time, when the newborn baby looks at you wide-eyed with wonder, moments after birth. If, in the excitement of getting to the hospital, you can remember to bring a camera, you will be able to take some photos of this precious time which you'll always treasure.

The more time the parents spend with the baby in the first hours of birth, the easier the bonding process. If, however, for some medical reason this is not possible, don't worry. Nature wasn't foolish enough to make this the only time when satisfactory bonding can take place! Just spend as much time cuddling and looking at your baby as soon as you are able to do so.

The first feed

The baby's sucking reflex is also at its strongest in the first few hours after birth, so when your baby is handed to you it is a good idea to put it to your breast. If, however, for some reason you feel you cannot do this (because you're too exhausted, too ill or just cannot make yourself), or if you try and the baby does not understand what to do, do not worry. Experts believe that this particularly sensitive period lasts for about twelve hours, so just try again quietly and gently a little later. I was worried when one of my daughters showed absolutely no interest in feeding just after she was born, but she had a feed a few hours later and subsequently proved to be the keenest breast-feeder of all, continuing until she was twenty-one months old!

To put your baby to your breast, if you're sitting up, cradle the baby in the crook of your arm, making sure that you're holding your baby with her body towards you so that she will not have to turn in order to reach your breast. Or, if you're lying down, roll on to your side and have the baby on her side, facing you, with her head near your breast. Gently stroke the side of the baby's face nearest your breast. This will make the baby turn towards your breast and purse her lips for sucking. As the baby does so, you can pop your nipple against baby's lips. Make sure that the baby has the whole of your nipple and some of the area around it, the areola, in her mouth. Alternatively, if you stroke the baby's lips with your nipple, playing with her and almost teasing her, she will get a bit excited and open her mouth wide. Then you can pop the whole nipple and some of the areola into her mouth. Never try to force your nipple into a little rose-bud mouth or the baby will slurp in the rest of it and cause you soreness. Also, watch that your breast isn't covering baby's nose and making breathing difficult: gently hold back your breast with your fingers if necessary to keep baby's nose free. If the baby is 'on' properly, her jaw bones or ears will wiggle as she sucks. Remember that the baby is learning the technique at the same time as you are, and it takes time for her to get used to taking your nipple. The baby that can snap on to a nipple from a foot away at three months, like a frog swallowing a fly, will, in my experience, fumble hopelessly and frustratingly at the beginning of each feed for the first week or ten days. For details of two most helpful booklets published by the NCT on starting to breast-feed and avoiding some of the problems, see page 215.

Establishing breast-feeding

After you've cradled your baby and given the very first feed, if this has been possible, the baby will be taken away to be bathed and dressed. You will be given that never-more-welcome cup of tea, and you'll be cleaned and tidied up and taken into the ward. The baby, comfortably tucked up in her cot, will be brought to your bedside, and, with any luck, will be able to remain there throughout the night as well as during the day. This means that you can put the baby to your breast as soon as she cries, giving her the welcome reassurance of your closeness and comforting her quickly. This frequent sucking, night and day, is important because it is the stimulation of your breasts by the baby's sucking which brings in the milk and keeps up the supply. For this reason, during these early days, the baby shouldn't be given any other liquid which could take the edge off her appetite and confuse her.

At this early stage the baby is not getting milk but colostrum, a creamy-coloured fluid which provides valuable extra protection against infection. This colostrum, and later your milk, contains all that the baby needs for the first months of life. The baby does not need anything else, even water, in addition. The colostrum is also valuable in that it helps the baby to excrete the meconium from her bowel. Meconium is a sticky black waste-product which builds up during the time the baby is in the womb.

The actual milk comes in a few days after birth. This might be the second, third or fourth day. The milk usually comes in more quickly with second and subsequent babies, but the timing depends on how much sucking the baby has been able to do. The more you have been able to feed the baby, the more your breasts will have been stimulated, and the quicker the milk will come in: although until it does, the colostrum will supply all that the baby needs. Don't listen to ill-informed nurses or anyone else who might tell you that you're 'spoiling' your baby by constantly picking her up and feeding her, or that she will get fat because of frequent feeds. On the contrary, you're doing exactly the right thing to ensure successful breast-feeding and a secure and happy start for your child.

When the milk does come in you may well find that you are really 'bursting' and the process is rather messy. This is nothing to worry about; just keep on feeding your baby completely on demand and your supply will quickly adjust to the baby's needs. If you find that you have so much milk that it gushes out too quickly for the new baby, making her splutter and choke, you can hold back the milk a little by holding your breast in your fingers, just above the areola, and pushing your breast gently upwards.

In the early days you may find that milk leaks from your breasts between feeds; even hearing the cry of a baby can trigger the 'let-down reflex' which brings in the milk, and cause this to happen. It is helpful to put a small pad of soft material, such as a small square of disposable nappy, inside your bra to prevent damp patches on your clothes, and to avoid wearing, say, pale blue denim shirts, where any leaking stands out a mile! Don't let these inconveniences put you off. They all pass rapidly as you and your baby get used to breast-feeding. Your breasts will shrink back to a much more normal size (even though they are producing large quantities of milk), they will not leak, and the whole process will become smooth, easy and delightful: very different from these early days of adjustment.

If your breasts become very full, they may get so firm that the baby has trouble in taking the nipple. If this happens, you will need to express some of your milk. It's also useful to be able to do this if your baby is born prematurely, so that she can be fed on your milk and, later, so that you can leave a bottle of your milk for the baby if you have to go out.

To express milk, hold your breast in one hand and use the other to stroke downwards towards the areola. Do this a number of times, to get the milk moving in the ducts. Then support your breast in the palm of your hand, with your thumb about half way up your breast. Run your thumb down your breast towards the areola, pressing as you do so. Do it gently, don't bruise the tissue. The milk will spurt out of the nipple. If you're doing this simply to rid yourself of excess milk, you can do it over a washbasin. If your milk is being saved, perhaps to feed your baby if she is premature, or for the hospital milk-bank, then you will need to catch the milk in a sterilized jug or tupperware-type container, cover and refrigerate or freeze it immediately. You will never completely empty your breasts, because as they're stimulated they make more milk; but you should stop when the milk is only coming out in drops instead of spurts.

Some experts give a timetable for baby's feeds, starting with two minutes each side and increasing by a minute a day to ten minutes. This is supposed to prevent sore nipples but most mothers get a short period of nipple-soreness whether they stick to a timetable or not, and to subject yourself and your baby to a time limit is confusing and unnecessary and not now recommended. It could mean that the baby does not get all the food and comfort that she needs and that your breasts do not get the stimulation they need to produce the right amount of milk. Remember, it is the baby's sucking which stimulates the milk and regulates the supply. Always let your baby decide how long the feed needs to last, but try to make sure the baby sucks from both breasts at each feed in the early days, while the milk supply is becoming established.

After the baby has finished feeding, dry your breasts carefully. If you do have problems with leaking, cover them with a small square of disposable nappy (not tissues, as they disintegrate). If you're having the soothing salt baths so often recommended after birth, don't forget to rinse your breasts with clean water. Dry carefully. Some people advise putting on some Massé cream or lanolin twice a day, but these are not really necessary as your breast produces its own protective secretions.

Something which many mothers experience – certainly most of the breast-feeding mothers I know – is sore nipples. This means that the first few seconds of a feed are agonizing as the baby grasps the nipple. After that, the pain passes: it does not last for the whole of the feed. If this happens to you, do not despair and feel you have to give up. The soreness will pass: sometimes this takes a day or so, sometimes longer, two or three weeks, and in fact the baby's sucking will help it to do so. It's a good tip to start feeding from the less sore breast; the baby's sucking will bring the milk into the other breast, too, so that the baby will not have to suck so hard to get started on the sore side. Calendula ointment, which you can get at health shops, is a natural and wonderfully soothing and healing ointment which you can safely apply to sore nipples.

The kind of soreness described is different from the sort which lasts throughout the feed and indicates damage or stress to the surface of the nipple. This can be very painful, but can heal quickly. There is helpful advice on this in the NCT booklets. You can also get excellent advice from an NCT breast-feeding counsellor: these counsellors are all mothers who have breast-fed their babies and they are most helpful.

Bottle-feeding

Unless for some reason you really loathe the idea of breast-feeding, I think it is a pity to start bottle-feeding until you've given breast-feeding a really good try. In this context, it's worth remembering that it can take up to six weeks or so to establish breast-feeding, not just ten days or a fortnight, which is what some mothers seem to assume. So do not be in too much of a hurry to give up; do give yourself and your baby time to learn the art. Nevertheless, even if you fully intend to breast-feed, it is useful to know about bottle-feeding.

Warm milk provides a perfect environment for bacteria; in addition, even the best formula milk does not contain the antibodies and natural immunity which passes from mother to baby in breast milk. So you have to be scrupulous about hygiene when making up the feeds, and the feeding bottles and all the equipment you use for measuring and mixing have to be sterilized after every use.

It's therefore worth buying a generous number of feeding bottles and two sets of measuring, mixing, bottle-cleaning and sterilizing equipment to enable you to rinse the bottles during the day or night as they accumulate. You can then have one grand washing-up session each morning and evening when you put all the bottles to sterilize during the day or night (see page 60). Bottles put to sterilize in the morning will be ready by the evening, those put to sterilize in the evening will be ready next morning. The sterilized bottles can then be taken from the sterilizer as they're needed.

The list of equipment below will allow you to do this with the maximum convenience:

8–10 feeding bottles: either plastic or glass, with caps or covers to protect the teats before use

2 measuring jugs with covers

2 funnels

2 5-ml plastic measuring spoons

2 plastic mixing spoons

2 plastic knives or spatulas for levelling off the spoonfuls of powder as you measure

2 bottle brushes

2 sterilizers or polythene boxes with lids – the boxes should be large enough to hold half the above equipment

bottle-sterilizing fluid

Choosing the type of milk

It's important to buy a milk which has been specially formulated for babies so that it is as much like human milk as possible. Don't be tempted to use ordinary cow's milk or evaporated milk which are not right for the baby's delicate digestion and could put too much strain on her kidneys. When deciding which type of milk to use, check that it is fortified with the vitamins the baby needs (and which she gets automatically from breast milk). Also read the making-up instructions to see how easy it is to use: many powders can be put straight into the bottle and shaken with boiled water, others need to be mixed first, and some formulas come in concentrated form, like evaporated milk, and are particularly easy to mix.

There are several baby milks which are made from plant sources and thus suitable for vegans; these include Formula S made by Cow and Gate, and Granolac and Plamil which you can get from health shops.

Making up the feeds

Have a kettle of boiled, cooled water ready. Wash your hands before touching the milk or sterilized feeding bottles. Take a measuring jug from the sterilizer, drain but don't rinse or dry. Pour exactly the correct quantity of cool boiled water into the jug. Measure, with scrupulous accuracy, the right amount of milk powder, and of sugar if the brand you are using requires this. Add to the water. Remove mixing spoon from sterilizer and stir mixture until blended. Place cover on jug and keep in fridge, or remove bottles from sterilizer, drain but don't rinse, and fill from the jug. Put the teats upside down into each bottle, cover with the caps and refrigerate until needed. Carefully cover the packet or tin of powder and store in the fridge.

If you're using a liquid formula, shake the can, wipe the top of the can, then sterilize by pouring some boiling water over it. Open the can with a sterilized can opener. Pour the correct amount into sterilized feeding bottles or mixing jug then add the right amount of water. Store in the fridge.

Always keep the made-up bottles of milk cold until the baby needs them, then stand the bottle in a jug or thermos flask of hot water for a few minutes. Remove cover from top of bottle, put the teat upright and test the temperature of the milk by inverting the bottle and letting some drops come out on to the inside of your wrist. The milk should feel just warm and should come out at the rate of several drops every second. If the flow is slower than this, use a red-hot needle to make the hole in the teat a little larger.

Giving a bottle feed

Cradle the baby in the crook of your arm so that she is cosy and close to you. Gently touch the baby's cheek nearest you; as the baby turns towards you, pop the teat into her mouth. Make sure you tilt the bottle well so that the milk fills the teat-end of the bottle, with no air gap. Pull on the bottle a little as the baby sucks, to keep up the suction.

Cleaning and sterilizing equipment
Never try to keep remainders of bottles warm, even for a short time. Throw away any milk that's left over and rinse out the bottle. In the morning and evening, when you have your washing and sterilizing session, wash all the bottles and equipment with hot water and washing-up liquid. Use a bottle brush to clean the inside of the bottles. Turn the teats inside out and rub them with some household salt to clean off all traces of the milk. Fill the sterilizer with fresh water and sterilizer solution. Place all the bottles and equipment in the sterilizer and cover, making sure that everything is below water level.

Burping the baby

After the baby has finished feeding, hold her up against your shoulder and gently rub or pat her back until she 'burps'. Make sure that the baby is straight; if she is curled up, her stomach will be squashed and the wind will not be able to come up. Some babies do not swallow much air as they feed, and not all babies need to burp at every feed, so don't worry if nothing happens. If you put the baby on her tummy when you put her into the cot, she will be able to burp later, if necessary, and won't choke if she brings up a little milk at the same time.

Don't worry either, by the way, if your baby does bring up some milk after feeds. This is quite normal and just means the baby has had more than enough! The only kind of vomiting you do need to take notice of, and report to your doctor immediately, is projectile vomiting, when the baby vomits with such force that the vomit shoots across the room. This may indicate a fault in the baby's stomach muscles which can be completely cured by a small operation.

4 Coping in the Early Days, 0–3 Months

It's a wonderful moment when you wave goodbye to the nurses and taken your baby home. But it's also daunting when you suddenly find that the responsibility for the welfare of that demanding and probably unpredictable small person now rests entirely with you. Added to this, you probably still feel tired and perhaps physically battered from the birth. Your hormones are in a state of transition, changing from a pregnant to a non-pregnant state and adjusting to breast-feeding.

Do not be surprised, therefore, if you feel fragile and weepy, just when everyone expects you to be feeling thrilled with your baby and on top of the world. This will come, but your body needs time to recover and adapt. Emotionally, too, you need time to think over and relive the birth, and adjust to your new role. Giving birth is a tumultuous experience and both you and your partner need to be able to 'talk it out' during these early, post-birth days. So do not set yourself any target during these early days except that of gradually getting back your strength and helping your baby to settle into a harmonious routine. It's worth knowing, too, that it takes about six weeks for the milk supply to become firmly established. Once you have been feeding successfully for this length of time, it takes a very great deal to upset things. But until then, this is another reason for making an extra effort to look after yourself by avoiding unnecessary stresses and strains and taking care not to get too tired. In this context, it's worth remembering that some cultures, for instance the Vietnamese, expect the mother to remain in seclusion for the first month after birth, which I think is a good idea. I think we in the West could learn something from these cultures; we try to be 'superwoman' and feel slightly guilty if we're not 'back to normal' within a few days of the birth. I certainly felt emotionally fragile and vulnerable for at least a month after my babies were born and wanted to remain at home, away from noise and crowds.

Babies aren't born with an instinctive knowledge of the difference between night and day, and few that I have met have sleeping and eating habits which conform in any way to the idea of 'four-hourly feeds' and the neat little timetables given in old-fashioned baby books. Most new mothers are surprised and puzzled by the frequency with which their baby cries and wants to be picked up and fed: quite different from the mental picture they may have of a baby lying serenely asleep in her cot for long periods of time!

The first few weeks can therefore be somewhat chaotic, and in my opinion you will weather them best – and get the most enjoyment from your baby – if you can adopt a very flexible attitude. Accept that a pattern and routine *will* emerge, but that you and the baby need to grow into this together and that the process cannot be hurried. I realize that this attitude is easier for people like me who haven't much sense of time, and rather enjoy doing things at odd hours, than for those who like a more organized, orderly existence. But trying to be too orderly and organized with a young baby is nerve-racking for all concerned. It is less harrowing if you can let the baby set the pace and fit your timetable into the baby's, rather than try to make the baby fit yours. Later, as you get used to the baby's pattern, you will find that you can manipulate it to some extent by either waking her for a feed or keeping her going for a bit longer before feeding.

Coping during the day

In these early days the baby will be happiest and you will probably cope best if you pick her up when she cries and offer a feed. Although this is the most natural thing to do, for some reason most people – and I was the same myself – have the feeling that the baby ought to sleep for longer and conform roughly to the idea of four-hourly feeds, each followed by a peaceful sleep! Then there are plenty of well-meaning people only too ready to tell you that you're spoiling the baby by picking her up, that the baby is only crying because 'she wants you to pick her up', and that 'the baby needs to exercise her lungs by crying'. But you cannot 'spoil' such a tiny baby, and her lungs do not need any exercise other than that which she gets every time she breathes. And yes, the baby probably is crying because she wants you to pick her up. But if you think about it, that, too, is natural, considering how close the baby has been to you for nine months. The physical closeness between you needs to continue, easing away very gently and gradually over the weeks and months.

So, when the baby cries, assume that she wants feeding, and put her to your breast, even if the last feed was as recent as half an hour ago. This frequent feeding will, as I have already said, stimulate your breasts to produce more milk, thus increasing your supply. It's because breast-feeding depends on this supply-and-demand system that breast milk, though a perfect food, does not sustain the baby for as long as formula milk. Breast-fed babies need feeding more often than those who are on the bottle, which I see as nature's way of ensuring that the transition from womb to independence should be a very gradual one. If you get a situation where it is essential that the baby should sleep for a period of three or four hours, for your own sanity, the preservation of your marriage, or some other reason, giving your baby 50–75ml (2–3 fl oz) of formula milk from a bottle (if she will take a bottle) will probably ensure this. It can also be a good idea to give a baby an occasional bottle of, say, boiled water, just to get her used to taking a bottle. But if you're serious about breast-feeding, this is best kept as a last resort, rather than be allowed to become a habit.

Of course, babies do cry for reasons other than that they want to be cuddled and fed, and as the days go by you will get to understand what the various cries mean and when, for instance, the baby is crying with irritable exhaustion just prior to falling asleep. But at this stage, when the baby is so tiny and you are trying to establish the feeding, I think it is best to try a cuddle and a feed first, before the baby gets so upset that she finds it impossible to feed. Remember that you can't overfeed a breast-fed baby and in many parts of the world feeding continues virtually all the time, with the contented baby carried in a sling at her mother's breast, able to have a little suck whenever she feels the need. It may well be the comfort of sucking, and the knowledge of your closeness, which the baby needs, rather than food. If you have a very 'cuddly' baby, you might find it helpful to use a sling – which you can make or buy – and carry the baby around with you.

If you feel that the baby is unduly restless, check that she is the right temperature. Being small, babies both lose and gain heat quickly and their hands are not always a good guide to their body temperature. So make sure that the baby is cosily wrapped up and keep the room as warm as you can: 75°F (24°C) is not too warm for a newborn baby. On the other hand, a baby can get overheated in a warm room if you pile on too many blankets, so you need to be vigilant to get it just right. But don't put the baby out in the pram for long periods of time. A tiny baby's need for fresh air is greatly overstated; it is much more important to see that the baby is warm enough, and a normal airy room can supply all the 'fresh air' that the baby needs.

Something else which can have a soothing effect on a restless baby is to wrap a shawl firmly around the baby, then tuck the covers firmly and cosily around her when you put her down in the cot. This gives the baby the feeling of being securely held. When the baby no longer needs to be so firmly tucked up, she will let you know by wriggling and kicking off the covers. If you have a very 'sucky' baby and find the almost constant feeding too much to cope with, you might consider giving the baby a dummy. Most new parents don't give their baby a dummy when it would be very helpful, for example for colic or during fretful evenings, because they are terrified that the baby will become addicted and they will never be able to get the dummy away. But the baby will give up the dummy of her own accord between three and five months old, when she is less desperate for comfort-sucking. We gave our eldest child a dummy and it was such a comfort to all concerned! She gave it up spontaneously at four and a half months when her first tooth was coming through. A dummy can be a great comfort to mother and baby alike, and I certainly recommend them as long as they're not used so excessively that they prevent the baby from getting all the physical comfort and cuddles she needs, and the frequent feeds which help to establish breast-feeding in these early days.

If you do use a dummy, keep it scrupulously clean by placing it in a container of water and feeding-bottle sterilizer when the baby is not using it. Never put any form of sweetener on the dummy and do not give the baby a dummy containing fruit juice or other liquid. These will interfere with the baby's demand for breast milk and may have a detrimental effect on the baby's teeth.

Don't feel that you have to give the baby a bath every day. A daily bath is fine if you have the time and if the baby likes it. But many newborn babies dislike their bath, and this, combined with a new mother's natural apprehension and awkwardness, can make the bath a worrying time for both. The baby will be perfectly all right as long as she is 'topped-and-tailed'.

To top-and-tail, simply wipe the baby's face gently with cotton wool moistened in a little cooled boiled water. Use a clean piece of cotton wool for each eye, starting at the inner corner and wiping gently towards the outside. Then, using ordinary warm water, gently wash and dry the baby's hands. Next, take off the nappy and wash the baby's bottom with warm, soapy water, rinsing and drying well. Finish with some vaseline or zinc and castor oil ointment to protect the baby's skin against damp nappies.

Some babies just seem to be born lively and if you happen to have one of these you will not get much peace. The baby certainly will not sleep for anything like as long as other babies seem to, and will want to see what is going on around her.

The way to cope with a baby like this is to let her be wherever you are, in the midst of the household clamour. Put the baby, where she can see you, in one of those little rocking cradle chairs or a convertible reclining chair, or prop the baby up in her cot or in a chair. Make sure that she is firmly supported with cushions and cannot slip. Talk to the baby often – the sound of your voice will be reassuring – and make sure there is always plenty for the baby to look at. Coloured mobiles are a good idea and are quite inexpensive to make using coloured card cut into shapes, or small colourful objects strung up from a hook in the ceiling. An alternative is to stretch a piece of rope across the baby's pram, like a washing line, and peg or tie on to it different items such as pieces of brightly coloured tissue paper, a string of bells, a piece of bright ribbon. Change the objects often to keep the baby's interest. Babies also like looking at coloured birthday cards or pictures pushed down the sides of the cot and pram. A musical box is often a great success with tiny babies. You could also buy a recording of simulated womb noises which has a calming effect on a restless baby: I believe a recording of an automatic washing machine, with its whirls and gurgles, has a similar effect; or, easier still, simply put the baby near the washing machine!

However hard you try you will probably get one of those days when the baby never seems to stop demanding and you feel at your wits' end. This is the time when it's so marvellous if you have a kind neighbour who understands this desperate feeling and will take the baby, immediately, for half an hour to give you a breather. But if you haven't such a neighbour, remember that ten minutes of crying never hurt any baby. Put the baby out of earshot, make yourself a drink, and set the timer for ten minutes. Then relax. You'll be surprised how different you feel when the timer goes and you return to the baby.

When you're struggling with a difficult baby who is lively, never sleeps and cries easily with frustration or boredom, it's sometimes helpful to remember that all the characteristics you find such hard work in a baby have a flip side: aggression = drive; obstinacy = perseverance; liveliness = interest in life, and so on. Babies who are very hard work become children who never cease to amaze and delight you. It's tempting to think 'oh for a dim baby who sleeps': but is that what you really want?

Coping during the evening

One of the most difficult times with a young baby is in the evening when many seem to have a fretful period just when you are tired and longing to have an hour or so to yourself. This, in my opinion, is where demand-feeding is such a help. The way I coped with this difficult time, which I had with all three of my daughters, was to get in a good supply of interesting books and magazines, make myself a soothing drink, sit in a comfortable chair with my feet up, and let the baby feed while I relaxed. It is a demanding stage and if you adopt my policy it does mean that your evenings are a write-off and it's useless to plan any social life, so you'll need the understanding and support of the rest of the family. But though it seems hard to believe at the time, this stage passes very quickly – within a few weeks – and you will probably look back on it with some nostalgia in the future.

You may well feel that there is not much milk left at the end of the day but, as I have explained, the baby's sucking action will stimulate the milk so the more the baby sucks, the more there will be. If, on the other hand, you think that the baby is wanting to suck for comfort, rather than for food, you might well find that a dummy could be the answer. I know it's not aesthetically pleasing, but it could make all the difference to your evenings. If you think that the baby is wanting to suck because she is hungry, and that the problem is that you're short of milk in the evenings, it is better to try to increase your own supply, if you wish to continue breast-feeding, rather than start giving supplementary feeds from a bottle.

Increasing your supply of milk

There are a number of ways you can increase your supply of milk.

Let the baby feed frequently, as already explained.

If your breasts feel full of milk during the morning, wake the baby if necessary for a feed. Demand-feeding is a two-way process, remember. The baby needs you, but you need the baby, too. Many babies will be only too happy to have a quick swig to relieve the pressure of overfull breasts, even if they do not want to wake up for a proper feed.

If the baby won't cooperate, it might be worth expressing this milk yourself, to encourage your body to keep on making milk for later in the day.

Make sure you are eating well yourself and, particularly, that you're getting enough food during the early part of the day. This is especially important during the first six weeks when the breast-feeding pattern is being established and you may well find you're ravenously hungry at times. Don't skip breakfast and lunch; stoke the boilers evenly, not a cup of tea for breakfast, a sandwich for lunch and a large evening meal. If you feel you haven't time to bother during the day, see the ideas in the recipe section for quick nutritious snacks and drinks. Many breast-feeding mums, myself included, find they have a craving for quite stodgy food made from wholewheat flour, such as bread and, dare I say it, things like wholewheat fruit cake, gingerbread and biscuits. We all know that too much sugar and fat are to be avoided, but all I can say is that from my own experience and from that of successful breast-feeding mothers I know, this does seem to be a time when wholewheat cake and biscuits are useful and they can be nutritious (see page 192). Warming spices are said to stimulate the milk flow, too, and these can be included in cakes, drinks and also in savoury dishes.

Make sure you're drinking enough; don't forget to take a drink whenever you feel thirsty but don't flood the tissues, which can reduce milk supply. Try to replace the fluid taken by the baby; drink something yourself when the baby does.

Try and arrange your day so that you do most of the essentials, like the washing and making preparations for the evening meal, in the early part of the day.

Conserve your energy in the afternoons. When the baby sleeps, you sleep too, if you can, or at least try to rest.

Having a young baby really is a full-time job, and a demanding one, so don't feel you're useless because you can't do anything else!

This applies even more if it's been a difficult birth, or if surgery was involved. If this was the case, take special care of your nutrition; try some of the vitamin-rich drinks on pages 107–13. And whatever kind of birth it was, don't set yourself impossibly high standards: rest and relax as much as possible in between dealing with the needs of the baby. Mentally give in to, and make the most of this intense but fleeting period: something that you will experience only once, twice, perhaps three times, during your life.

Remember that it takes several days to increase your milk supply (you won't see much result in less than forty-eight hours), so keep on trying for at least two weeks before you judge the results.

Evening colic
In the evening very many babies seem to have the restless, fretful period described, when they cry more than usual, and often parents think that the reason for this is 'colic'. When a baby has colic (which often does not start until the baby is about a month old), the baby appears to be in real pain, drawing her knees up to her stomach, crying and sobbing uncontrollably. Nothing seems to comfort the baby for any length of time; doctors do not know the cause of the problem and there seems to be little that they can do to help. Gripe water is sometimes helpful or you can make a dill water by steeping a teaspoonful of lightly crushed dill seeds in a couple of tablespoons of boiling water, cooling and straining. A dummy can also be helpful; one of my daughters would become calm for a while with a dummy dipped in gripe water. Warmth, from a well-wrapped hot water bottle, put near (but not on top of) the baby's tummy, can also help. And some mothers find merbentyl, from the doctor, works for true colic. But one of the troubles with real colic is that there seems to be so little you can do. You keep trying things, and these seem to work for a short time, then the screaming and drawing-up of the legs starts again and you're at a loss as to what to do. You can try gripe water or homemade dill water, but if it's real colic these may have little effect.

If your baby really has got colic, it is *not* because of something you're doing wrong. It's just one of those inexplicable things, and you will have to face the fact that you're going to have very difficult evenings for a few weeks, giving the baby what comfort and reassurance you can. This is extremely taxing and demanding, and it will help if you and your partner can take turns to cope alternately with the baby throughout the evening. The only really comforting thing I can say is that colic rarely lasts for more than eight weeks and invariably stops, usually quite suddenly, by the time the baby is three months old.

Coping at night

When you put the baby down for the night, it's a good idea to try and create a different atmosphere from day-time sleeps. Put the baby in her cot in the bedroom; make sure that the room is warm and dark, with perhaps just a low light so that you do not have to switch more light on and risk waking the baby when you go to bed or when you're dealing with night feeds.

Unless you are very lucky, once you do finally get to sleep you will probably be awakened at least once during the night. However, breast-feeding does make the night-time feeds relatively easy to cope with, and if you can manage to feed the baby while she is still sleepy the chances are that you will both fall asleep again very quickly. So don't let the baby cry for any length of time; have her near you, if possible right by your bed so that you only have to reach over and pick her up. You can then feed the baby easily, almost in your sleep, and both go back to sleep again quickly.

Unless you have a very fussy baby, most experienced mothers agree that it is much better not to try and change a nappy in the night unless it is obviously causing discomfort. If you feed quickly and then put the baby straight back into the cot without messing about with creams and nappy pins, you will both have a better chance of getting back to sleep again.

If you go along with your baby's need for night feeds, you will find that, just like the day, a pattern gradually emerges. The time between feeds will grow longer. You may find, as I mentioned before, that you can manipulate the timing of the night feeds by waking the baby for a feed just before you go to sleep, so that then, with any luck, you get an unbroken period of sleep during the early part of the night.

5 The Baby, 3–6 Months

Gradually you'll find the chaos and unpredictability of the early baby days pass; you and the baby will evolve a harmonious routine, and the baby will respond increasingly to you and begin to take a lively interest in the world around. Babies begin to be fun at around this age and there are various things you can do to entertain the baby and help her to develop mentally. Research has shown that the more time you spend playing with and talking to your baby, the more quickly she will develop and the more intelligent she is likely to be. Looking after a baby is certainly a great deal more interesting, rewarding and enjoyable if you have some ideas for stimulating and playing with the baby.

The baby will still enjoy the things described on page 66: coloured pictures on the walls beside the cot or pushed down the sides of the cot and pram (well secured, or the baby will grab and eat them as she gets older); coloured mobiles to look at; a musical box to listen to. In addition, when the baby is around two to three months old, she will enjoy being able to reach out and touch a fluffy ball or rattle suspended from the pram hood or from a piece of dowelling lashed across the cot. Those suction rattles which you can buy to stick to the high chair or the wall beside the cot are also great fun for the baby, as is a 'mobile gym', which consists of various toys for the baby to push and pull, mounted on a plastic bar that you tie across the cot.

From about three months the baby begins to enjoy exploring things with her hands. She likes to touch a rattle, a string of wooden beads or cotton reels or a bunch of keys. Give your baby plenty of different objects to handle and study, varying the shapes and textures: a piece of soft material, a small furry toy, some crackly shiny paper rolled into a ball, tissue paper to handle and tear, small empty cardboard boxes and plastic bottles, pieces of sponge, cardboard tubes from loo rolls, empty egg boxes, rattles made by putting some dried beans or lentils into a plastic container with a firmly secured lid. Again, watch for eating; the baby son of a friend of mine used to eat his older sisters' comic and they would come out in his nappy still readable! And I have vivid memories of one of my babies eating handfuls of small pebbles on the beach. I did not realize she had actually swallowed any until I saw what came through in her nappy the next day. Not recommended! Still, neither my daughter nor my friend's son suffered any dire consequences.

A baby this age will also enjoy playing with your kitchen utensils; a plastic bowl is fun to fill with ping pong balls and, a little later on, saucepans are great to bang with a wooden spoon.

From about the age of three months, as soon as she can hold her head unsupported, the baby can be put into a baby bouncer. This is a little fabric harness attached to a piece of springy rubber which fastens to a hook in the ceiling or to a clip over the door frame. As the baby puts a toe on the ground, she will bounce. A baby will get a great deal of pleasure from bouncing several times a day – and you will be free for a few minutes to get on with something nearby.

If yours is a lively baby, you'll be used to having the baby beside you in her little rocking chair or propped in another suitable chair. All babies will now need this opportunity and will watch happily as you go about your tasks. The more there is to look at, the happier the baby will be.

Continue to talk to the baby frequently and repeat the sounds which the baby makes to you. The baby will love the rhythm of songs and rhymes and soon respond to games of 'peep-bo' action rhymes, such as pat-a-cake, 'this little piggy went to market' and 'round and round the garden'. The Ladybird rhyme books are useful for jogging rusty memories, and the BBC Playschool records are also good. The baby will also love to sit on your knee and look at the pages of a brightly coloured picture book.

During this period (between three and six months) the baby will learn to roll over; to sit unsupported for a few seconds and to prepare to crawl; she will love to pull herself up on your knee and bounce about, supported by your body and reassured by your closeness. You can encourage your baby's physical development by letting her have periods lying on a rug in a warm room or sunny garden with the minimum of clothing (or none at all).

Although they're demanding, babies at this stage can be enormously rewarding and fun. The more you cuddle, talk to and play with the baby, the more you will get out of the relationship, and the quicker the baby will develop. Giving the baby this close attention is *not* 'spoiling'; it is helping the baby to develop as fully as possible, mentally and emotionally.

Some mothers seem to enjoy all this naturally; others find themselves distraught with boredom and frustration, resenting and begrudging every demand. Because they're emotionally drained by the effort to meet the baby's increasing needs, they hold back, trying to keep something in reserve. The baby soon senses this and becomes more demanding as a result. So a vicious circle begins.

If this is a problem for you, I can only say that, paradoxically, the more quickly and fully you meet the baby's demands, the more contented and 'easy' the baby will be and the more chance you'll both have of being reasonably happy. I strongly advise this course of action, though you may receive advice to the contrary, such as 'you'll spoil the baby', or 'the baby mustn't be taught to think she can have everything she wants'. I do not agree with these statements and in my experience the reverse is true, as I have explained above. The more certain the baby is of having her needs met, the *less* anxious and demanding she will become. She will learn from an early age to have a basic confidence in the goodness of life and the expectation that her emotional needs will be met. In any case, a baby of this age is far too young to be able to use her 'power' over you in a calculating way; she is just aware of her needs – for food, comfort, stimulation, love – and that you are the person from whom these will come.

I personally found I coped best if I considered the baby to be my full-time job during the day, not planning to do anything else except absolutely essential shopping and cooking, and the minimum of necessary cleaning. Then I would look forward to an hour or so of my own in the evening when the baby was in bed. I certainly found it helpful to make sure I had plenty of activities lined up to keep the baby happy and amused.

It can also be a very great help to get out and meet other mothers who are in a similar position. Coffee mornings, such as those run on a local basis by the NCT, give the social contact which can be such a morale-booster at this time. I certainly found this to be so, as it is comforting and therapeutic to be able to swap experiences and realize you're not alone in what you're going through. Teaming up with another mother so that you each take it in turns to look after both babies on a regular basis can also be most helpful. It's less emotionally draining to look after two babies for, say, a couple of hours, knowing that later you will get a couple of hours to yourself.

Teething

Towards the end of this six-month period the first tooth or teeth may appear. The timing does vary a good deal, with some babies remaining toothless until around a year, so do not worry if the half-birthday passes without any sign of a tooth.

Babies often have some degree of discomfort when cutting their teeth, more especially with the back teeth, which appear during their second year, than with the first front teeth. The baby may find it comforting to chew on something hard: a teething ring or, from about six months, a piece of apple, raw carrot, bread or rusk (see page 212) which she can hold in her hand and feed herself with. Although this is a very good practice and will probably keep your baby happy for some time, never leave a baby alone with food like this because of the danger of choking. If something does get stuck in the baby's throat either hook it out quickly with your finger or turn the baby upside down and smack *gently* in the small of the back.

Incidentally, you don't need to stop breast-feeding when the baby's teeth appear. Strangely enough, these do not hurt. This is because the baby's mouth is filled by your nipple and the areola around it, and so the jaws are open, not closed. Sometimes the baby may inadvertently bite at the end of a feed, after she has finished the process of feeding and is just continuing to 'play' with your breast. Prevent this by removing your breast as soon as the baby has finished feeding; the baby will quickly learn not to bite.

6 The Baby, 6–12 Months

During this period the baby will sit up unaided and also begin to crawl; it is an exciting time of rapid physical development. You can encourage the crawling process by putting the baby down on her tummy on the floor, preferably unrestricted by a nappy. If you place a desirable object a little way in front of her, the baby will soon learn to get to it by crawling forward. It has been found that the crawling phase is tied up with the baby's intellectual development, so do not be in a hurry to get your baby walking. For this reason it is not a good idea to put the baby into one of those 'walkers' which supports the baby in a standing position and allows her to propel herself around the room.

Once the baby begins to crawl competently, nothing will be safe. For your own peace of mind, and the happiness of both the baby and yourself, it's a good idea to look at your home with new eyes, removing anything tippable, breakable or pullable. The baby will want to be playing around on the floor wherever you are, so it's worth taking the time to make these areas safe. Make sure there are no loose electric wires and that the points are safe; that fires are securely guarded; that scissors and other sharp instruments, bottles of cleaning fluid and medicines are stored well out of reach. Try to use mainly the back burners on your cooker if the baby is playing around by you while you're cooking. Have some way of blocking off the stairs. It takes a bit of an effort to do this, but is worthwhile because once it is done you can relax and let the baby race around and explore in safety. You will be able to get on with things while the baby plays around beside you. Put the baby in old, comfy clothes so that she can get as grubby as she likes without worry. The more unrestricted she is, the better for her development. For this reason it's not a good idea to leave a baby in a playpen for long periods of time (though a playpen can be useful for short periods of time, to provide a short respite from being 'on guard' all the time – long enough to answer the phone or drink a cup of tea, for instance). In general, however, it's not easy for a baby to learn to be an enquiring, hopeful and enterprising adult if her efforts to explore are frustrated or, worst of all, rewarded with a slap. A baby of this age is too young to understand the meaning of punishment and will just be puzzled that the person to whom she looks for comfort and love has suddenly lashed out and hurt her.

Of course, however carefully you 'baby-proof' your home, there will inevitably be times when she will get something she mustn't have, or manage to open a drawer which had hitherto been beyond her. When removing the forbidden treasures, it saves a great deal of hassle and upset if you can divert with an alternative: 'You mustn't have that, but here's something that's just as much fun.' If there are certain things in the house which you do not want your toddler to touch, by all means explain this to her simply, but you will have to do so over and over again. It's unrealistic to expect a baby of this age to remember, or to override her own will/need/ desire; she is incapable of this until she is coming out of toddler- hood. Until then, her will and yours may coincide, but she is not capable of doing something to please you, or to annoy you. I think that expecting a baby or toddler to be aware of the consequences of her actions, when she is too young to understand, is at the heart of many of the problems which mothers have with them.

Once the baby is crawling around you may wonder about hygiene, especially as her presence means you're probably not able to clean the house as thoroughly as you'd like! Yet, as long as basic standards of hygiene are maintained, the baby will be fine. Keep the food-preparation areas of the house clean, also the bathroom, and keep pet food (which, like any food, can harbour bacteria) out of the way. Get the vet to worm your pets before the baby starts to crawl and then regularly every few months.

However clean you keep the house, once the baby is crawling

around she will certainly need a bath in the evening to clean off the results of the day's explorations. Bathtime can be great fun with a variety of plastic ducks and containers, a lightweight plastic jug and funnel and a watering can for discovering the fascinations of water-play. After the bath these can be kept in a large plastic bowl or a plastic net bag slung over the taps.

During this period the baby will still enjoy the toys mentioned in the previous chapter (pages 72–3). She will particularly appreciate toys which make a noise, such as drums, some bells or a tambourine. She will also have fun with toys which she can operate herself: a simple, not-too-noisy jack-in-the-box, a jumping man on a string, a wooden hen which clucks as you pull it along. Look for robust toys that are simple to operate. Once the baby can sit up, she will get a great deal of pleasure from playing in a sandpit. It's not difficult to make one by filling a large, shallow, wooden or plastic box with sand, or by digging one in the garden. Make sure you get 'river sand' from a garden or hardware shop. Supply some small light spades or big spoons and a variety of containers for filling with sand, and always cover the sandpit with a lid or piece of polythene when it's not in use to keep cats out.

It's amazing how many toys a baby of this age accumulates, and you'll need to find somewhere indoors to keep these. A practical solution is a wicker or plastic laundry basket or a shallow wooden box into which you can heap everything after use, and from which it's easy for the baby to get what she wants during the day. Alternatively, you could use cheap, oblong, washing-up bowls which can be stored on open shelving later on. Whichever you use, keep the box, basket or bowls of toys in the kitchen, sitting room or wherever you are during the day, so that the baby can play close to you.

'Close to you', not to say all over you and into whatever you're trying to do, is the operative word during this stage. You will find that you cope best if you can accept this, plan your day with this in mind, and draw your baby into as many of your activities as possible. This can be frustrating, because jobs will be accomplished much more slowly and less efficiently. The key is not to set your standards too high; mentally to slow down your own pace and remember that all the time you're in fact doing *two* jobs – the practical task in hand, and the most important job, that of looking after the baby. The baby will love to help dust the furniture and sweep the floor; to stand up at the sink on a chair and dabble her hands in the water while you're washing up; to play with some pastry trimmings when you're baking. A trip to the shops can be the highlight of her day, especially if you talk to her about all the interesting things you pass on the way, and the goods you're putting into your trolley. Let the baby feel the bulkiness of a loaf of bread, the coldness of a packet of frozen peas, the lightness of a packet of crisps. Then when you get home, let her help you to unpack your bags and put the things away. Make every effort to build up a feeling of the two of you as a team, coping with things together – and having fun together – rather than getting into the habit of thinking of the baby as an encumbrance to what you want to do. A warm feeling of companionship created now will grow and stand you in good stead for the years ahead.

What with the clutter which a baby makes about the house and the demands she makes on your time, unless you have a great deal of domestic help it's impossible to maintain high standards of tidiness and housekeeping. This is easier if you're not terribly houseproud than if you're naturally inclined to worry about every mark. But you will be far happier – and so will the baby – if you can resign yourself to having just a quick tidy-up once a day than if you feel all the time that things ought to be tidier. Why? Who for? The most important thing at this stage is for the baby to be happy and for you to feel relaxed and able to enjoy her.

When my babies reached this stage I found that, in contrast to the early baby days, I coped best if I had some sort of routine to the day. Periods of play with bricks, sand, water, quiet times looking at picture books and playing with other toys interspersed with walks to the shops, the park or to feed the ducks, and a blessed period in the late morning or early afternoon when the baby slept and I had a few moments to myself.

Although this is in many ways one of the most rewarding stages it is also one of the most exhausting. You are quite likely to find, as I did, that coping with a lively 'into everything' baby, doing the essential shopping, making an evening meal and keeping the house in some sort of rough order occupies all your day and takes every ounce of energy, leaving you exhausted in the evening with very little to show for your labours except one happy, thriving, rosy-cheeked little person.

Emotional needs

It is during this period when babies become fiercely attached to their mother (or mother substitute) and can become very upset every time they lose sight of her, even if it is only for a few moments. This phase passes quickly if you give the baby the reassurance of your presence which she needs. She cannot understand that if you go away you will come back: she does not know enough. The more you try to stop her from clinging by going away, the more insecure and fearful she will get. Make an effort to get the baby used to another person as well as you: a relative or neighbour whom she knows well enough to be left with when you have to go away for short periods. On the other hand, it is obviously best if you can keep the times when you're away from the baby to the minimum while this 'clinging' period lasts. By giving the baby what she needs during this intensely emotional period you'll help it to pass as speedily as possible. You will also create an emotional security which will enable your baby to make happy and fulfilling relationships throughout her future life.

Weaning

Breast milk supplies all that the baby needs for the first six months of life. So, if the baby is happy and thriving, there is no need to think about introducing any solids until she is six months old. If, however, after four months of age the baby does not seem fully satisfied with milk, you might try giving her a first taste of food. The danger with introducing solids early is that the likelihood of an allergic reaction is increased as the baby's immature digestive system cannot readily cope with the food.

The first spoonfuls are really just to get the baby used to the taste and feel of solid food in her mouth. Do not think of them as a real source of nourishment at this stage, as the baby still needs milk-feeds for that and also for the emotional satisfaction which is derived from sucking. Gradually, however, the baby will eat a little more solid food, take correspondingly less milk, and drop one feed after another. The introduction of solid food should be gentle and the transition from an all-milk diet should take several months. If you start when the baby is around six months, the weaning will probably be largely complete by the time she is a year old.

The gradual weaning process goes something like this. When the baby is around six months old, offer the first taste of solid food, perhaps half a teaspoonful, at one of the main milk-feeds corresponding to breakfast, lunch or supper, whichever is the most convenient for you. If you are planning to go back to work but want to continue to breast-feed – which is perfectly possible – obviously you will want lunch to be the first meal at which the baby gives up her breast-feed and just has solids.

Whether you give the first taste of solid food before or after the milk-feed is up to you and, perhaps more especially, the baby. Generally speaking, it is perhaps better to give solids before the milk-feed if you can so that, as you gradually increase the quantity of solids, the baby will satisfy herself and forget about the feed. However, there is no point in trying to give solids if the baby is hungry, wanting comfort and crying for a feed. Better to let your baby feed first and then give the taste of solids at the end.

Traditionally cereals were always the first solid food given to babies. However, these can cause allergies if given too early, and many people now favour fruit and vegetable purées as first baby foods. The following foods are the ones I would choose for a baby's first taste.

Mashed ripe avocado: this may seem strangely rich and luxurious, but is an excellent and nutritious first food and commonly used as such in other parts of the world (and you can finish what the baby leaves for your own lunch)

Finely mashed ripe banana: cut the banana in half and scoop out the line of black seeds with the point of a knife the first time, if you're really fussy, though I've never bothered with this

Apricot purée: make from dried apricots which have been soaked and cooked, if necessary, as in the recipe on page 208

Finely grated apple, pear or carrot: use the finest side of the grater so that you have a soft, juicy pulp

Sieved or puréed cooked apple: sweetened with a little honey or raisins (see recipe on page 184)

Sieved or puréed cooked carrot: don't add any salt

Prune purée: soak the prunes, simmer until soft and then sieve. Watch the baby's nappies as this could be too much of a laxative

Mashed potato: made without salt or butter

Natural yoghurt: sweeten with a little honey or fruit purée

Wholewheat cereal: buy this at a health-food shop or soak one of the well-known brands, such as Weetabix, or wholewheat bread, in a little warm milk. Don't add sugar. Again, watch the nappies. If the fibre proves too laxative, causing a sore bottom, experts advise trying a more refined variety.

Purée of brown rice: use ground brown rice, from health shops, and make as on page 209

Porridge: make this from rolled oats, according to the ground rice recipe

Smooth lentil purée: see recipe on page 210

Some people suggest introducing a new food every week. Certainly if you have any history of allergies, asthma, hay fever or eczema in your family it is advisable to continue with one food for at least four days before trying another, watching the baby carefully in case there is an allergic reaction. The foods most likely to provoke this are milk, eggs, wheat, bananas, tomatoes, strawberries, nuts, chocolate and some food additives and colourings, particularly the bright yellow colouring used in orange squash and many sweets.

Be prepared for the fact that the baby may well spit out your lovingly prepared offerings. Do not worry and try not to react in an emotional way. After all, the baby is not depending on this food for nourishment at this stage. Try again another day, persisting gently. There is no hurry.

As the baby gets used to the flavour you can gradually increase the quantity so that after a few weeks your baby is having perhaps a tablespoonful of food at a time. You can then begin to introduce new tastes of food at other main feeds so that eventually feeds which correspond to breakfast, lunch and supper are composed entirely of solids.

You will find that as your baby takes more solid food at each feed the demand for milk will decrease. The baby will suck from you for a shorter time and your milk supply will decline correspondingly: the reverse of the process which enabled you to produce enough milk in the early days. You will probably find it takes two or three days for your body to catch up with the baby's decreased demand, and your breasts may feel rather full, but this transition period will quickly pass.

You will gradually be able to drop first one feed and then another. The bedtime feed should be the last to go. Do not be in a hurry to wean the baby from the bliss of this; it is important for the closeness to you and the emotional satisfaction which the sucking gives. So by the time the baby is around nine months old, she may well be just having this bedtime feed and any feeds which you might give during the night if the baby wakes. Many babies have spontaneously given up the bedtime feed by the time they are one year old but many have not. We managed to wean my youngest baby off her evening breast-feed when she was twenty-one months old. I say 'we' because we did this by my husband putting her to bed for a week, and also attending to her in the night as necessary.

Regarding night-time feeds at this age, some people believe that it is not a good thing to encourage feeding during the night after, say, six months, when the baby probably doesn't need the feed for nourishment but may just be acquiring an enjoyable habit which may drive you to distraction later on. Some recent research at the Hospital for Sick Children, Great Ormond Street, would seem to confirm this view. Case studies showed that wakeful babies who were dealt with kindly but firmly and decisively while being left in their cot developed settled sleeping patterns within days. I personally found the easiest way to get my (very wakeful) youngest daughter back to sleep was to give her a quick breast-feed – but now I wonder whether I was making a rod for my back and, were I to go through the experience again, I would certainly try this firmer, more decisive approach.

Some people suggest weaning a baby from the breast on to a bottle when you start giving solid food. I do not see any point in this unless you want to stop breast-feeding for some reason. If the baby is happy, you're willing to go on and all is going well, it seems better to continue breast-feeding for the few remaining months, although once the baby has given up all the day-time feeds you might like to give a bottle for the final night-time feed to free you to go out in the evenings.

Making more of a meal

Once the baby has become used to the feeling of solid food in her mouth, there is no need to be so particular about puréeing the food. In fact it is good for the baby to get used to a bit of texture in food at this stage. I soon found I only needed to mash the food for my babies although I have heard of other babies who were very fussy about this.

As the baby gets more and more used to her solid foods and comes to depend on them as the main source of nourishment, you can enrich them with other protein ingredients. For example:

egg yolk or finely grated cheese which can be mixed into the hot
    vegetable purées (the heat of the vegetable will cook the egg)
a little tahini (sesame cream) or peanut butter (not too much as they
    are highly concentrated)

cottage cheese
chopped or sieved hardboiled egg
mashed cooked beans and other pulses
tofu
finely powdered nuts – do them in a clean coffee grinder or use
ground almonds
mashed nut roast or lentil savoury
wheat germ

Eating plans, 9–12 months

If your baby takes well to solids you will quite soon find that a little
of what you, as a family, are having will be eaten easily and
naturally by your child. Do watch that the baby's portion is not
too highly seasoned, though. Sometimes it's possible to take out
a small quantity for the baby before adding spices and seasonings.

At this stage, between nine months and one year, the baby will
probably have an eating plan which goes something like this:

Breakfast
Apple purée with wholewheat cereal or extra finely grated nuts (see
above)
or
Baby muesli mixed with finely grated apple
or
Porridge with extra milk and a very little honey
or
Wholewheat cereal with finely grated nuts and raisins
Wholemeal toast or bread with a scraping of butter or vegetable
margarine and just a little honey or yeast extract – try and get
an unsalted one from health shops
Milk (not skim, which is unsuitable), soya milk or fruit juice to
drink

Mid-morning
Water or fresh fruit juice diluted with water and perhaps a piece
of apple or carrot

Lunch
Puréed vegetables with protein ideas as suggested
Mashed cauliflower cheese
Puréed lentils and some vegetables
Mashed nut or lentil savoury with puréed or mashed vegetables
Mashed potatoes with grated cheese, peanut butter or finely grated nuts
Baked beans mashed with wholemeal bread
A pudding of freshly grated apple, mashed banana or ground rice or millet milk pudding or apricot fool (see recipes)

Tea/supper
Orange or apple juice, diluted with water, or milk
Wholemeal bread and vegetable margarine or butter with a little unsalted yeast extract, smooth peanut butter (page 133), honey, no-added-sugar jam or the apricot purée on page 208
Cottage cheese with grated carrot and tomato and wholewheat bread
Scrambled or lightly boiled egg with fingers of bread or toast, with or (preferably) without butter or vegetable margarine
Jacket potato mashed with milk and grated cheese
These can be followed by a little cereal or some fresh fruit for pudding

Before bed
Breast-feed

Feeding problems

Some babies are very fussy eaters which makes mothers worry, wondering how they can tell if their baby is getting enough food. If the baby is healthy, lively and growing, then enough food is being consumed, though sometimes you may feel that the amount is hardly enough to keep a sparrow alive. Paediatricians assure us that children of this age will not starve in the face of food and the most important thing for you is to remain calm and not allow a tense atmosphere to build up at mealtimes.

Do not worry if your baby really does not like some food, because you can usually find another source of the same nutrients: see Chapter 1. It is far better to stick to foods which you know the baby likes – even if this means her diet is boringly repetitive for a time – and avoid battles of will. All children go through the stage when they learn the power of the word 'no', and it can be very wearying unless you learn to divert them and offer a choice instead of single suggestions which they can veto.

It also helps if you can encourage your baby to feed herself from an early age. Protect the baby with a sensible bib – the plastic ones with pockets in which to catch spilled food are good – and the floor under the baby's chair with newspaper, which looks messy but can be thrown away and renewed, or with plastic sheeting, which has to be wiped clean. Put the food in front of the baby and let her feed herself. This will be an undeniably messy business at first.

Do not worry if the baby eats her foods in the 'wrong' order or mixes things up; and do not set too high a standard. The baby will enjoy being independent and with practice her competence will grow.

Sleeping

Babies need less sleep in their second six months, and if yours is a particularly lively baby, you may soon find the baby's sleeping time during the day reduced to two short periods or one longer one (if that!). Whether the baby actually sleeps or not, it's a good idea to plan your day to include two brief 'rest' times, when you settle the baby into her pram or cot. Provide plenty of interesting things for her to look at or get on with quietly until she actually falls asleep. But if she doesn't go to sleep, make sure that you do not leave her to 'rest' for too long, so that she becomes bored and unhappy.

During this period, often around nine months, many babies go through a phase of being difficult at bedtime. A baby who has hitherto gone to bed quite happily will become clinging, screaming and crying and not wanting you to leave the room. This is really a night-time extension of the emotional clinging described on page 81. Once again, the quickest way to get through this stage is to give your baby the comfort she needs and assure her of your physical closeness. But at the same time you have to ease yourself away, or you will find yourself trapped in the situation of having to sit with the baby until she falls asleep – which could be quite a lengthy process.

Prepare for bedtime by making the hour preceding it as happy and loving as possible. Try to avoid upsets and conflicts at this time. Warn your baby that bedtime is approaching and build up a bedtime routine that you follow each day: perhaps a pleasant bath, playing with the ducks and other toys in the water, then a trip downstairs to say 'goodnight' to the rest of the family. Then up to the bedroom for a story, a 'goodnight' kiss for the favourite toys, a kiss and a cuddle for the baby and a favourite lullaby. After this, tell the baby that she must go to sleep, that you're going downstairs but you'll pop back in a moment or two. Keep popping back and also calling out encouragingly as necessary. If your baby really won't release you, it may be helpful if you can arrange to delay your parting by planning to tidy and put away clothes in her bedroom so that you're close while she is going off to sleep. Go out when this is done, but again, keep popping back reassuringly often, and certainly either pop back or call out reassuringly if the baby cries out. This way you'll build up her confidence that you're still there and that her needs will be answered, and gradually the difficult phase will pass. Whatever you do, try not to pick the baby up and bring her downstairs, even once, as this will create bad habits for the future. You've got to be loving but firm; which isn't always easy – I think we're often afraid to be firm, but it can be done in a kind and loving way, reassuring the baby at the same time that you're still close and caring, but also that you're not going to pick her up or play!

Sometimes a restless, wakeful pattern may develop during the night around this time, too. This can be extremely wearying when you're physically exhausted by the demands of a lively and increasingly mobile baby. Often there is no apparent reason for the wakefulness, but it's worth checking the obvious things such as whether the baby is warm enough – one of those 'baby bags' will keep her cosy if she kicks the covers off; whether there is some noise that is waking her up and, if so, whether you can improve the situation by moving her bed to a different position, putting up thicker curtains or even double-glazing; whether she is waking because of nappy rash making her bottom sore (protect her with a thick layer of nappy cream and a one-way nappy at bedtime). You might also like to try giving the baby a few drops of a harmless, natural, sleeping remedy at bedtime. There's one called Avena Sativa Compound which is a herbal remedy manufactured by Weleda and obtainable from health shops.

If none of these things makes any difference, it's quite tempting to think that the baby is waking herself up on purpose, just to be annoying. This of course is impossible: just think how difficult it is for adults to wake themselves up by strength of will, let alone a tiny baby! Neither can babies of this age do things for effect, as I've said, either to annoy or please you. They can, however, do things because your response amuses or interests them, so don't reward a wakeful baby by being chatty or scolding.

There may be some subtle reason for the baby's restlessness. It may be that she unconsciously feels the need for more cuddling, or is upset by something in her day's routine. Sometimes this night-time waking is associated with trying to wean a baby too quickly, for instance, when she still needs the comfort of sucking. So mentally check on these things next. If none of these applies – or the problem is no better – there is nothing you can do but accept the situation and make the best of it. It may be helpful to find out whether it works best to leave the baby to cry for ten minutes – some give up and go back to sleep – or to go in immediately. If you have the kind of baby that you have to go in to, you'll probably find it best to get up quickly, the moment she starts to cry. She will probably go back to sleep quickly as soon as she's reassured of your presence, and you too can go back to bed and, with any luck, also fall asleep again quickly. My third child woke up usually five times a night until she was eighteen months old – when she suddenly started sleeping through – so I have great sympathy for this problem. I coped by going to my child as soon as she cried, rocking her back to sleep with a breast-feed – which was usually extremely quick – and then thankfully going straight back to sleep myself. It's amazing how quickly one learns the ability to go to sleep after these night-time interruptions. They are tiresome: but, like most of the difficult stages, they *do* pass!

Some babies wake at a most unsociably early time in the morning and this too can be a problem. But it's no good expecting a baby refreshed by a night's sleep to go back to sleep again. It's better to arrange for the room to be lit with a low-power nightlight and leave some suitable toys within reach. It may even be worth making the effort to get up and give her a drink or change her nappy, if this will mean she will play happily in her cot for a while and give you a little longer in bed.

7 The Baby, 12–24 Months

This second year marks the transition from babyhood to the toddler stage and great progress is made. It's a delightful and interesting period during which the baby learns a large number of new skills and becomes even more of a companion.

In many ways the one- to two-year-old is still very much a baby; yet at the same time she feels a growing awareness of her own identity and need for independence. It can therefore also be quite a turbulent time for you both, and humour and a philosophical attitude, plus plenty of patience, will help you to cope. The secret of coping well with this period – and indeed throughout childhood – lies in being sensitive to your child's need; being careful not to push her towards independence too quickly, yet at the same time avoiding treating her too much as a baby and so causing rebellion and aggression.

You are still the centre of your toddler's life and she is just beginning to learn that she wants to please you. Before, she was not aware of you as a person separate from her. Yet, on the other hand, she feels an increasing need for independence and may suffer an inner conflict as a result. You can help here by gently teaching her to be independent, being sensitive both to her need and her capability, helping her to cope with each stage as soon as she is ready, but without pushing her faster than she can manage to go. Praise her for being, full stop. That is, praise her for what she is, not what she does. That way she cannot fail, and she will learn what pleases you by your attitude, not your words. Watch that you do not inadvertently put pressure on her so that she feels she has to strive to reach an at times impossible standard in order to get your love and approval.

Children – even within the same family – are so different and

I think one of the secrets of successful handling is to be able to let your child set the pace while being on the lookout for signs that she is ready to be helped to cope with a new skill.

I know this is a controversial subject, but I must say I found it very helpful with my own children to know a little about their type of character and temperament from their horoscope. I found the information which this gave extremely valuable; in fact I wouldn't like to have to bring up a child without it! The information is general enough to avoid moulding the child in a preconceived way but gives many helpful pointers for bringing the best out of the particular temperament which, by the age of two, it's becoming obvious that the baby has. The address to write to for more information is on page 213.

Play and development

During this year physical skills increase dramatically and you'll need to expand the boundaries of the safe play-area accordingly. Try, as before, to make the area safe and baby-proof rather than have the worry of the possibility of the toddler getting into danger or mischief, or the strain of constantly having to restrict her or say 'no'. Get clear in your own mind where you will draw the boundaries, but have as few of these as possible. Remember, toddlers have short memories, strong emotions and live in the present; and a child of this age simply does not understand the difference between 'being good' and 'being naughty', so do not expect the impossible.

Make sure your toddler is not thwarted in her movements by clothes which are stiff, uncomfortable or too big. They should be soft and comfortable to wear so that they don't restrict vigorous play; have easy-care things which can go straight into the machine and don't need ironing. At this stage of rapid growth it's a waste of money to buy special clothes for best. Buy normal clothes which you can use for best when they're new, then for every day after that. Cheap and cheerful, easy-to-do-up, washable, drip-dry clothes are the best choice from both your point of view and the toddler's, with a washable all-in-one anorak suit for cold days and wellington boots for sploshing through puddles. Apart from the fun of playing with sand, water and mud, a toddler can only concentrate on one thing at a time and if she is busy trying to climb up a muddy bank she simply won't be able to think about keeping her clothes clean.

Make the most of the child's urge for independence and help her to achieve it. Show her, for instance, how to slide safely off the bed by rolling on to her tummy and sliding off, feet first, and how to negotiate the stairs safely. When you're showing your toddler how to do something, make a conscious effort to slow your pace right down. We take familiar actions such as doing up a button or tying shoelaces so much for granted, forgetting how many small actions are involved in the process. Try doing things with the other hand from the one you naturally use to get an idea of how the toddler, with her lack of coordination, feels. Break up a process into tiny stages and teach these to your child slowly, one at a time, so she gradually learns the complete skill.

Every day is full of discovery for a child of this age and it is a revelation to see the apparently boring daily walk to the shops through her eyes. You suddenly find yourself noticing all kinds of things such as fire engines and car-transporters, and it becomes so automatic to point these out that you may find yourself doing so to an amazed company of adults when the toddler isn't with you! Even visits to the supermarket can be fun if you let the baby take a lively interest in your shopping. Talk about the things you're buying, enlist her 'help' over what you need, which item to choose, then let her examine the things as you put them in the trolley. She'll find it hard to wait to sample your purchases, but perhaps she'll be allowed to try something once you've got everything safely through the check-out.

As a change from the daily routine, toddlers love trips to different places: a visit to a farm-trail or zoo, a trip on a train or the top of a bus for a change from the car. These will stimulate her interest and give plenty for her to look at and point to. You can help the development of her language by talking about the things that you see, drawing her attention to different colours, shapes and sizes.

Help your toddler begin to make decisions by asking her to make simple choices (and stick to them!): 'Which sock shall we put on first?' or 'Which colour brick shall we pick up next?' It's best to avoid presenting her with complicated choices where she hasn't the experience to know which she'd enjoy most and will worry that she's going to make, or has made, the wrong choice. To ask 'Would you like to go to the park and play on the swings or go to the pool and feed the ducks?' is probably too difficult for her; it's better to say 'Let's go to the park and play on the swings' and save the alternative for another day.

It's good experience, too, for a toddler to have the chance to play with another child of her own age. If you can seek out a neighbour with a toddler perhaps you could take it in turns to have each other in for a couple of hours each week. 'Playing together' at this age amounts to the toddlers watching one another, but for the most part each getting on with their own ploys with you intercepting fairly frequently when one pinches the other's toy. Babies become very possessive with their toys at this stage, and your efforts to take something away will be met with howls of rage. So always divert quickly by offering an alternative or distracting the baby on to some other interesting activity. If this regular get-together works well, you may find that after a while your toddler will stay and play without you, giving you a most welcome hour or so of peace.

Regarding suitable toys for this age group, the toddler will still have fun with all the toys mentioned in the previous sections. Water play, the sandpit and play with bricks will be specially enjoyed; also cups or rings which stack into or on to each other and teach the first concept of bigger and smaller. With these the toddler will also be able to learn the meaning of into and on to, inside and outside, through putting things into boxes and playing hide-and-seek with her toys. Toys which push and pull along are great fun; also a posting box, which teaches the recognition of different shapes; simple jigsaws and tray jigsaws. A large cardboard box which she can crawl into will give a toddler hours of fun.

Discipline and punishment

What is discipline? Not punishment, but teaching. I, personally, am not in favour of smacking children, especially when they're as young as this. When a baby or young child looks to you for love and comfort, it seems to me to be abusing that trust suddenly to inflict physical pain on the child. And it's equally bad to discipline a young child by putting emotional pressure on her; pretending to cry if she does something naughty; giving warmth and love when she's 'good' and being cool when she's 'naughty'. A baby of this age is too young to understand the consequence of her actions, that if she pulls the tablecloth everything will fall on to the floor, if she drops your best vase it will break. Even if she did understand these things, her memory is short and a toddler lives very much in the present. So although she may promise she won't pull out your drawer of sewing things yet again – and mean it at the time – a few minutes later she has forgotten all about it and will undoubtedly do it again later. To scold her for it would be confusing because she has genuinely forgotten about the last time – and is too little to understand the concept of 'promise', anyway. It's better to tie up the drawer or move your sewing things to a higher one and put some bricks or other toys in the one she keeps opening.

This second course of action is the best because not only does it harmonize the situation, it also gives the baby the satisfaction of being able to do something positive for herself – to open 'her' drawer and get some toys out. This demonstrates one of the secrets of handling a toddler well: avoid confrontation whenever possible and look for a positive way of dealing with a situation. If she gets something she can't have, divert her with something else that's 'much more fun'; if you want her to fetch something and she says 'no', challenge her to a race: 'I bet you can't get it before I've counted to five.' She'll get it, 'win', and have fun at the same time.

Once you get into the habit of thinking in these ways it's surprising how many potentially difficult situations can either be diverted or turned into fun. This way you will be able to discipline your toddler by making her want to do what you want her to.

Coping with tantrums

If you adopt the policies described above, you will (mostly) avoid exhausting tantrums and the bond between you will grow stronger and warmer as you 'have fun' together and generally meet life's challenges as a team. However, there will almost certainly be times when you or the baby are tired and you mismanage or misjudge the situation, or when things are complicated by some other factor and a tantrum results. Once the child is in the grip of a tantrum she is coping with an emotional force too strong to control. She is incapable of stopping and may be frightened by the strength of her own emotions. She may shout and scream and rush around the room, crashing into anything that's in her path, or throw herself to the floor, kicking and screaming. She may even stop breathing and appear to lose consciousness for a few moments, though paediatricians assure us that children cannot permanently damage themselves this way.

Keep as calm as you can when dealing with this situation; try at all costs to avoid screaming back at the child even though you, too, feel at the end of your tether. When she is in the grip of a tantrum she genuinely cannot do anything about it. Take immediate steps to remove anything dangerous or breakable. It's generally best to hold the child firmly either on the floor, if that is where she has ended up, or on your lap. Then she will gradually calm down and can be cuddled and comforted. If holding the child just makes the tantrum worse, just remove anything dangerous or breakable from her way and wait until she has calmed down before cuddling and comforting.

Once the child has recovered, behave as if the tantrum had never happened. Go ahead with whatever you had planned; don't alter your plans in response to the tantrum or stop doing something which the child enjoys as a punishment. Let the child see that you accept the tantrums as something which she cannot help. Try not to reward the child with extra (disapproving) attention after a tantrum; do not let her see that you're upset by them or worried about the possibility of her having one in an awkward place. Try not, for instance, to treat her any differently if she has a tantrum when you're visiting a very prim and proper friend than you would do if it happened at home. I realize that's difficult, because most of us are so aware of the disapproval of others and this does change our behaviour; but that's the ideal to aim for! Continue to do your best to handle the toddler in such a way as to avoid tantrums as much as possible, but to treat them as calmly and matter-of-factly as you can when they do arise, and very soon you'll find you're through this stage, and the 'terrible twos' will be a thing of the past.

Rests and sleep

This is often an in-between period for rests as the toddler makes the transition from two naps a day to one long one and you will probably find yourself constantly adjusting your timetable and the hour at which you have your lunch. Many toddlers end up having quite a long rest in the middle of the day, then as they get older they want to go down for this later and later so that it begins to interfere with bedtime. When this happens the toddler may have to be woken from her rest before she's really ready. Most toddlers hate being woken up from a rest and you'll need to allow time for cuddles and comfort as you gently help the toddler to ease herself into the waking world again.

Bedtime can still be a problem for a baby of this age, with difficulty in getting her to settle down and go to sleep and begging you to stay. I do not hold with the 'leave her to cry whatever happens' philosophy; I think it's best to aim for an extension of the policy described in the previous chapter. Follow a soothing bedtime ritual, as described on page 89, spend a little time tidying or pottering about, in or close to the toddler's bedroom, then say a final 'goodnight' and go. But be prepared to go straight back if the toddler starts to cry seriously (as against one or two sleepy cries). When you go back, you do so to reassure the child that you're still there, that she hasn't been deserted. Having done this in a cheerful but firm manner, go out again. If you keep this up long enough she will get bored, yet at the same time she will finally drop off to sleep with the comforting thought that you're not far away and that you care. Some toddlers take an awful long time to get bored! So aim to do the very minimum necessary to reassure the child: you have to use trial and error to discover what this is. Trying though it is at the time, this phase, like all the difficulties of childhood, does pass and you'll soon have forgotten all about it.

Sometimes during this year a toddler goes through a phase of waking up, terrified, with nightmares. When these happen, all you can do is to go to her, cuddle and reassure her until she's comforted, then settle her back to sleep. But it's worth thinking about any possible reason for these disturbances. Is she going through a particularly stressful period, for some reason? And if so, can you think of any ways of taking the pressure off? Perhaps she is being weaned too quickly or is anxious because of overzealous toilet training? Perhaps her routine has been disrupted in some way, or maybe there is a new baby in the family? Be extra loving and tolerant, take special care to keep to her familiar routine and generally 'baby' her a bit, until her sense of security returns and the nightmares pass.

Toilet training

Since a child is physiologically unable to control her bladder and bowels until fifteen months at the very earliest, there's absolutely no point in starting toilet training, or even buying a pot before then. The important thing with toilet training is to relax – and let it happen. Remember that babies vary a good deal in the time it takes them to get 'clean' and 'dry', and if your particular child is later than some it's no reflection on either you or her. It's not a race, and all babies get toilet-trained eventually even though you begin to wonder whether yours is going to be the great exception!

To start with, babies are totally unaware of their bodily functions. Then, suddenly one day, when the toddler is about to have a dirty nappy, she notices the physical sensation and realizes that something is about to happen, though not soon enough to stop. Once this has happened, you can produce the pot and suggest next time she might try going in that instead of in her nappy. But don't appear too eager: try and be fairly unemotional about the whole thing. You will find your toddler will get the idea.

Toddlers are able to control their bowels first; bladder control takes longer, because the sensation of passing water, especially into a damp nappy, isn't so noticeable. It will help the toddler to become aware of what is happening if you can let her have some periods of play without a nappy. It's a great help if this stage coincides with some warm summer weather and the toddler can run about in the garden without a nappy. Then, when she makes a puddle, she will suddenly notice what is happening. However, don't expect too much too soon, because noticing what is happening and actually being able to control it and reach the pot in time are two different things. You'll need plenty of patience, clean pants and damp cloths to wipe up the many puddles. But gradually your toddler will get the idea of telling you – probably by clutching herself strategically – when she's about to make a puddle, and hang on long enough for you to reach the pot or loo. You can, by the way, get a special children's loo seat which fits over the ordinary one. Unless your toddler is frightened of the loo, I don't think these are worth bothering with. It's better, in my opinion, to help her to get used to coping with the ordinary loo as soon as possible.

Once you've got to this stage, I think it's best to abandon nappies in favour of towelling pants during the day, using a nappy just at night and if you're going out and don't want the risk of a puddle. You can buy special 'trainer pants', made of towelling bonded to an outer, plastic layer, and some people like these. I personally think they're difficult to wash and dry and prefer plenty of (cheaper) towelling pants.

Much as you're longing to be rid of nappies, do try not to get emotional about toilet training. If you show pleasure when your toddler manages to use the pot, she has the means of displeasing you, and by this stage also the capability of using it. If you're having problems, not showing you're either pleased or displeased can defuse the situation. Accept it calmly when the toddler uses the pot, but equally accept that there are bound to be many 'accidents' too. Try to be even-tempered about these, and certainly don't scold the toddler for them; she isn't doing it on purpose just to be annoying, and she will get dry. Once she does, you'll find when you go out that you've simply swapped nappy-changing gear for a pot which you'll be taking everywhere with you, until she's got enough control to hang on while you find a loo. People who haven't had this experience can have no idea how this searching-for-loos stage slows up shopping expeditions and other trips: but, again, it doesn't last long.

Mealtimes

When a toddler is a faddy eater, I think it's best to let her eat when she wants to, rather than insist that everything has to be eaten at proper mealtimes. Don't worry that this will lead to bad habits; children are remarkably adaptable and she'll adjust to normal mealtimes later. I also think it's best to concentrate on giving the fussy toddler the food she likes, rather than insist on her eating things she's not keen on, with battles, and probably failure, as a result. Faddy children often do much better with raw finger food which they can eat with their fingers, rather than 'proper' meals. They also frequently want to eat what appear to be funny mixtures of foods, or to have these in an unconventional order. But what does it matter if she wants cold red kidney beans with raisins or cold potato with peanut butter? As long as they're nutritious foods, why not? If you adopt this easy-going approach, while continuing to eat your own meals as normal, giving her some when it's something she'll eat and alternatives when it isn't, the phase will quickly pass.

The secret is not to get emotional about the situation (a) because you're worried about your toddler's health or (b) because it's hurtful to have your food refused. It simply isn't worth making an issue over food, or allowing a difficult situation to develop. In fact, as in all things concerning your child, it's your relationship with her that's the most important thing. This is what you're building up and what will endure long after you've forgotten the horrors of broken nights, tantrums, food fads and puddles on the carpet! Always put this relationship first; before a spotless house, before rigid timetables, before battles over food or anything else, and you will be rewarded by the deepening bond of understanding and companionship which will develop between you.

Part II

Introduction

As I've already mentioned, the quality of the food you eat when you're pregnant or preparing for pregnancy, and afterwards when you're coping with the demands of a young baby, is of vital importance. Yet tiredness and nausea during pregnancy, and tiredness and lack of time after the baby is born, do not make this the easiest time for cooking. What you need, therefore, in my opinion, are simple, easy recipes based on the most nutritious foods, and this is what I aim to provide in this section of the book.

Choice of ingredients

As you've probably already noticed when reading Chapter 1, some foods are particularly rich in essential vitamins and minerals and it's worth using these as often as possible. Although some of these ingredients are quite expensive, many others are not. Cereals, wholewheat bread, pulses, potatoes, peanuts, cheese, milk and eggs, also vegetables and fresh fruit in season, are quite reasonable. The nuts and seeds are more pricy, but these are used in relatively small quantities and, remember, if you're vegetarian, you're saving money by not buying meat and fish. So, overall, I do not think you will find this way of eating particularly costly. It will almost certainly work out cheaper than a meat diet including convenience foods.

Choice of recipes

In order to qualify for inclusion in this book, recipes had to be nutritious, health-giving, and easy to make. The ones in the quick-recipe section had to be able to be made particularly easily. I have vivid memories of the many times I've prepared a meal with one hand, while comforting a crying baby by holding her over my shoulder with the other. As well as these very quick recipes, I've included a section of recipes which freeze well, so that you can stock up the freezer before the baby arrives. You'll also find recipes for nutritious salads and soups, with suggestions for making both into main courses; nourishing drinks you can whizz up to sustain you when you're breast-feeding; packed meals, easy wholefood cakes, biscuits, and high-energy sweets for taking to the hospital with you; healthy puddings, and a few special baby foods for weaning.

Drinks

Drinks can be an excellent source of nourishment when you're pregnant and not feeling much like either cooking or eating, or when you're breast-feeding and need to keep up your energy with the minimum of fuss. You will find these drinks most beneficial if you can sip them slowly while you relax or feed the baby.

In addition to the drinks given here, it's a good idea to keep a large jug of water in the fridge, chilling. You will need to drink water to replace lost fluid when you're breast-feeding (see page 68), and tap water is more pleasant when it's really cold. Even better would be tap water which has been passed through one of those filters which you can now buy, and this of course purifies the water too.

Apricot, Orange and Almond Whizz

This drink, and the one which follows, are particularly good to have after a Caesarean operation or when you've had a number of stitches, because they contain vitamins A and C which help the wounds to heal, plus iron to help replenish supplies depleted through bleeding. The apricots do need soaking beforehand (this applies even to those which say they're ready to use, in fact I don't see any advantage in paying more for these). If you like this recipe, though, it might be worth soaking a larger quantity of apricots and keeping the remainder in the fridge, so they're ready when you need them.

MAKES ONE 250-ML (10 FL-OZ) GLASS

50g (2 oz) dried apricots – unsulphured ones from the health shop
    are best
200ml (7 fl oz) pure orange juice
1–2 teaspoons clear honey
25g (1 oz) blanched almonds
1 tablespoon wheat germ

Wash the apricots carefully in warm water, then put them into a
bowl, cover with boiling water and leave to soak for a few hours,
or overnight if possible. Then drain the apricots and put them into
the blender with the orange juice, honey, almonds and wheat
germ. Whizz for about 60 seconds, until smooth. Pour into a tall
glass.

Apricot and Orange Nectar

A lighter drink which, like the previous one, supplies vitamins A
and C, and some iron and calcium, to help heal tissues after the
birth.

MAKES ONE 250-ML (10 FL-OZ) GLASS

50g (2 oz) dried apricots – unsulphured ones from the health shop
    are best
200ml (7 fl oz) pure orange juice
1–2 teaspoons clear honey
1 teaspoon brewer's yeast powder

Wash and soak the apricots as in the previous recipe, then put into
the blender with the orange juice, honey and yeast and whizz to
a purée. Pour into a glass and serve. This is good with some ice
cubes added in hot weather.

Banana Milk Shake

This drink, adapted from the one Barbara Griggs gives in *The Home Herbal*, is, as she says, a palatable way to take nutritious brewer's yeast powder, and rich in iron, calcium and B vitamins.

MAKES ONE 250-ML (10 FL-OZ) GLASS

1 banana, peeled
200ml (7 fl oz) milk or soya milk
2 heaped tablespoons natural yoghurt or vegan yoghurt (see page 191)
2 teaspoons brewer's yeast powder

Peel the banana and cut into rough chunks, then put into the blender with the rest of the ingredients. Whizz until smooth and frothy; serve at once.

Carob Shake

The carob gives this a deliciously rich chocolaty flavour as well as providing iron and calcium. This is another particularly good drink to have when you're feeling drained and in need of a quick boost of energy, and is a good way of taking milk or soya milk if you don't like drinking them in their natural state.

MAKES ONE 250-ML (10 FL-OZ) GLASS

1½ teaspoons carob powder
1 teaspoon honey
1 tablespoon skim milk powder or soya flour
200ml (7 fl oz) milk or soya milk
pinch cinnamon

Put the carob, honey and skim milk powder or soya flour into a small bowl and blend to a smooth paste with a little of the milk or soya milk. Heat the rest to boiling point, then pour on to the carob mixture, stirring well. Pour back into the pan and heat for a moment or two, to make it piping hot, then serve as it is, or pour into a blender and whizz for a few seconds if you want a foamy top.

Fortified Milk

This is another way of making milk palatable if you don't like drinking it plain. The addition of skim milk powder gives the milk a lovely rich taste, without adding many calories, as well as increasing the calcium. This one glass of fortified milk has double the calcium of an ordinary glass of milk. Other ingredients can be added according to taste: a little honey or a pinch of cinnamon or both, for instance.

MAKES ONE 250-ML (10 FL-OZ) GLASS

200ml (7 fl oz) milk
2 heaped tablespoons skim milk powder

Simply put the ingredients into a blender and whizz together. You can heat the milk first if you would prefer a hot drink.

Lassi

This drink from India is refreshing in hot weather, but also nourishing because of the protein and calcium in the yoghurt. It can be made salty or sweet, according to taste. If you want to increase your milk supply, try adding a teaspoonful of the seeds of fennel, dill, cumin, caraway or aniseed to this mixture. These are traditional herbal remedies for shortage of breast milk, and also act as a general tonic and antidepressant.

MAKES ONE 250-ML (10 FL-OZ) GLASS

1 big tablespoon natural yoghurt or vegan yoghurt (see page 191)
200ml (7 fl oz) chilled water
a pinch of salt; or 1–2 teaspoons clear honey and pinch of cinnamon; or a few drops of triple-strength rose water; or 1 teaspoon seeds, as mentioned above, steeped in a tablespoon of boiling water and cooled

Put the yoghurt into a glass and gradually stir in the water. Add the salt, or honey and cinnamon, rose water, or the water in which the seeds were soaked. (You can add the seeds, too, if you like, but this isn't essential.)

Miso Pick-Me-Up

A hot, savoury drink containing B vitamins.

MAKES ONE 250-ML (10 FL-OZ) GLASS

250ml (10 fl oz) hot water
1–2 teaspoons miso
2–3 tablespoons chopped watercress
salt

Put the hot water into a glass and stir in the miso, watercress and salt to taste.

Yoghurt and Orange Flip

This is a favourite drink of mine, pregnant or not. It's rich in vitamins A, B and C, and also contains calcium. It's particularly good after a Caesarean, or if you've had to have stitches, because the vitamins help the healing process, and it's also calming and revitalizing.

MAKES APPROX. ONE 250-ML (10 FL-OZ) GLASS

1 orange, peeled
150ml (5 fl oz) natural yoghurt or vegan yoghurt (see page 191)
a little clear honey, optional

Break the orange into segments and place in blender. Add the yoghurt, then whizz for 30–60 seconds, until fairly smooth, and add a little honey to taste, if you like. There will still be some chunky pieces of orange, but these give the drink a pleasant 'body' and provide extra fibre.

Herb Teas

Herb teas can be very pleasant and beneficial. The herb tea bags you can get from health shops are convenient to use and come in a wide range of varieties. They contain enough herbs to make a pleasant drink rather than a herbal medicine; for a stronger effect, use two tea bags to a cupful of boiling water. Or you can make your own herb tea from dried or fresh herbs. Herb teas which are particularly useful for pregnancy and childbirth are peppermint, for digestive problems, and chamomile, which is soothing and sleep-inducing and can be cooled and given to a restless baby, too. Peppermint, chamomile, lime or meadowsweet tea, taken first thing in the morning, can be helpful for morning sickness. Raspberry-leaf tea is a traditional and well-tried herbal treatment during pregnancy and can be safely taken, unless you've been doing a great deal of physical exercise and have very well-developed stomach muscles, in which case its muscle-toning effect might be too much. Drink a cupful of raspberry-leaf tea three times a day during pregnancy and the postnatal period.

MAKES ONE 250-ML (10 FL-OZ) CUPFUL

1 teaspoon dried herbs – peppermint, raspberry leaf, lime, chamomile or meadowsweet: from health shops, or see page 213
250ml (10 fl oz) boiling water
a little honey to taste, optional

Put the dried herbs into a cup and pour in the boiling water. Cover and leave to infuse for 4–5 minutes. Strain if you like, and sweeten slightly to taste if necessary.

Soups

Soups are easy to make. If you doubt this, try the lentil soup, the preparation for which takes about 10 minutes; or the quick butter bean and tomato soup, or the leek and potato soup, which can also be produced in minutes.

When you're pregnant, especially in the early days, soup may be just what you fancy, and homemade soup can be a good source of nourishment. You can make it more filling – turn it into a main course, in fact – by serving it with wholewheat bread or rolls, or hot wholewheat garlic bread.

To make garlic bread, you need a wholewheat stick or small, oval, wholewheat loaf. Slice the loaf without going right through the bottom crust, so that all the slices hold together. Beat one or two large crushed garlic cloves into 125g (4 oz) butter or polyunsaturated margarine, then spread the slices of bread on both sides with this. Press the loaf together, wrap in foil, and bake at 200°C (400°F), gas mark 6, for about 20 minutes, until the butter has melted and the crust of the bread is crisp. Serve immediately.

Sesame toast is also good with soup. To make this, toast wholewheat bread on one side. Butter the untoasted side, sprinkle generously with sesame seeds and toast under the grill until golden brown and crisp.

Easy Borsch

This is quick to make, using ready-cooked beetroot from the greengrocer. To make it into a main course, serve with grated cheese or the savoury seed mix on page 171, and garlic bread, cooked brown rice or a baked potato. It's also nice topped with a spoonful of natural yoghurt or, for a touch of luxury, soured cream. Borsch can be sprinkled with some caraway or dill seeds, if you like them, and these are a natural remedy for increasing the milk supply.

SERVES 4

2 large onions, chopped
2 tablespoons oil
225g (8 oz) cabbage – spring cabbage, primo or savoy, washed and shredded
450g (1 lb) cooked beetroot in its skin, from the greengrocer

1 425-g (15-oz) can tomatoes
300ml (10 fl oz) water
1 tablespoon tomato purée
1 tablespoon vinegar
salt, pepper and sugar

Fry the onions gently in the oil for 7 minutes, until almost soft but not brown. Then add the cabbage and cook for a further 3 minutes, stirring often. Meanwhile, slip the skins off the beetroot, using your fingers, then rinse the beetroot under cold water and cut into dice. Add to the onions, along with the tomatoes, water, purée and vinegar. Cook gently for 15 minutes. Season with salt, pepper and sugar.

To freeze Cook completely, cool and freeze for up to 2 months. To use, allow several hours to defrost, then heat gently, stirring.

Butter Bean and Tomato Soup

This is quick to make, using your own frozen butter beans (see page 135) or a can. It's nutritious enough to serve as a main course and even more so if you add a dollop of natural yoghurt, a spoonful of savoury seed mix (page 171) or some grated cheese for extra calcium. Good with wholewheat rolls or garlic bread, or a baked potato. Like Borsch, this soup is also nice topped with a spoonful of natural yoghurt or, when the budget allows, soured cream.

SERVES 4

2 large onions, chopped
2 tablespoons oil
350g (12 oz) home-cooked
   butter beans, or a 425-g (15-
   oz) can

1 425-g (15-oz) can tomatoes
1 tablespoon tomato purée
salt and pepper
sugar

Fry the onions gently in the oil for 10 minutes, until soft but not brown. Drain the butter beans, keeping the liquid. Add the butter beans and tomatoes to the onions. Make the reserved liquid up to 300ml (10 fl oz) with water and add to the pan, together with the tomato purée. Cook gently for about 5 minutes, until everything is heated through. Season with salt, pepper and a little sugar.

To freeze Cook completely, cool and freeze for up to 2 months. To use, allow several hours to defrost, then heat gently, stirring. Do not freeze if you're using butter beans from the freezer to make the soup: the texture will not be good.

Thick Leek and Potato Soup

Warming and soothing, this can be served with grated cheese or the protein seed mix on page 171; or it can be eaten as it is, sprinkled with lots of chopped parsley, with a protein course such as biscuits and cheese, yoghurt, muesli pudding or a handful of nuts and raisins to follow.

SERVES 4

15g (½ oz) butter
1 tablespoon oil
1 large onion, chopped
900g (2 lb) potatoes, peeled and
cut into chunky pieces
700g (1½ lb) leeks, washed,
trimmed and sliced

600ml (1 pint) water
1 vegetable stock cube
salt and pepper
chopped parsley, optional

Heat the butter and oil in a large saucepan. When the butter has melted, put in the onion and fry gently for 5 minutes. Then add the potatoes and leeks and fry gently for a further 5 minutes, stirring often. Pour in the water, crumble in the stock cube, stir and bring to the boil. Then cover and leave to cook gently for about 15 minutes, until the vegetables are just tender. Check seasoning, then serve, sprinkled with chopped parsley if you like.

Main Course Lentil Soup

Very soothing and nourishing and another excellent source of iron. This soup is very popular with babies I know, and was the first food I gave my youngest daughter when she was six months old. Serve with warm wholewheat rolls, or garlic bread made as described on page 114.

SERVES 4

1 onion, peeled and chopped
15g (½ oz) butter or
margarine
1 garlic clove, crushed
225g (8 oz) split red lentils

1.2 litre (2 pints) water
1–2 tablespoons lemon juice
salt and pepper
chopped parsley, optional

Fry the onion gently in the butter or margarine for 10 minutes, until softened. Then add the garlic, lentils and water. Bring to the boil, then simmer gently for 15–20 minutes, until the lentils are soft and pale coloured. You can either beat the soup with a spoon, to break up the lentils a bit, or liquidize, for a smooth, creamy texture. Add lemon juice and seasoning to taste; return to the pan and reheat before serving. It's delicious with some chopped parsley sprinkled over the top.

Watercress Soup

Watercress is rich in calcium and iron, and when cooked you'll find it a soothing and delicious way of taking a good dose of these minerals: I find it a marvellous tonic when I'm feeling tired.

SERVES 4

450g (1 lb) potatoes, peeled and cut into even-sized pieces
1 litre (1¾ pint) water
2 vegetable stock cubes
2 large bunches watercress

1 tablespoon potato flour or cornflour
150ml (5 fl oz) milk
½–1 teaspoon miso, optional
salt and pepper

Put the potatoes, water and stock cubes into a large saucepan. Wash the watercress, separating the leaves from the thick stalks and chopping the leaves. Reserve 2 tablespoons of the leaves. Add the rest to the saucepan, together with the stems. Bring to the boil, then simmer gently for about 15 minutes, until the potatoes are tender. Liquidize. Mix the potato flour or cornflour with the milk and add to the soup, stirring. Simmer soup for a further 5–10 minutes. Add the reserved watercress leaves and the miso if you're using it. Season with salt and pepper.

Salads

There's no magic about cooking which makes hot food more nutritious. A salad which you've quickly put together can be just as nutritious – often more so – than a 'good cooked meal'. So if you don't feel like cooking when you're pregnant, or if salads are more convenient for you to organize when you're busy with the baby, don't feel you're depriving yourself or your family of any vital nutrients: on the contrary.

Salads can be made from most raw vegetables except potatoes, aubergine and Jerusalem artichokes, and a salad made from vegetables which are in season can be very economical. For speed, I generally mix a quick oil and vinegar dressing straight into the salad bowl, then put in all the salad ingredients and mix gently. A salad like this can be served as it is, or with a spoonful of a creamy dressing in addition. The two which I've given below contain useful amounts of calcium and other nutrients.

SALAD DRESSINGS

Yoghurt Dressing

Plenty of parsley added to this increases its calcium and iron content and gives a pretty colour. I also like this very much served with hot nut and pulse savouries.

MAKES ABOUT 300ML (10 FL OZ)

300ml (10 fl oz) natural
  yoghurt
1–2 heaped tablespoons finely
  chopped fresh herbs,
  especially parsley, also chives
  and mint

1 tablespoon lemon juice
salt and freshly ground black
  pepper

Put the yoghurt into a bowl and stir in the chopped herbs, lemon
juice and salt and pepper to taste.

If you don't eat dairy produce Use vegan yoghurt, see page 191.

Variations Add some grated cucumber too, or leave out the herbs
and use two tablespoons finely chopped red or green pepper, or
some coarsely grated carrot and a few raisins.

Not suitable for freezing

Tofu Dressing

This is a bit like mayonnaise but considerably more nutritious,
since it contains useful amounts of iron and calcium, amongst
other things. If you're not sure what tofu is, see page 153.

MAKES ABOUT 350ML (12 FL OZ)

1 300-g (10½-oz) packet tofu
  – from health shops
2 teaspoons wine vinegar
1 teaspoon dry mustard
1 teaspoon barbados molasses
  sugar

2 tablespoons olive oil
salt and freshly ground black
  pepper

If you've got a liquidizer, simply put all the ingredients into the
goblet and whizz together until combined. Alternatively, put the
tofu into a bowl and whisk until smooth, then add the vinegar,
mustard and sugar and whisk again. Then beat in the oil, a little
at a time. Season with salt and pepper. This is also nice with some
chopped fresh herbs or spring onions added.

Not suitable for freezing

How to Sprout Beans and Seeds

Sprouted beans and seeds are highly nutritious and full of the life-force of the emerging shoot. I like them at any time, but they seem particularly appropriate to eat when you're pregnant, especially if you find ordinary cooked pulses a little heavy or indigestible. You can sprout most pulses; my favourites are chickpeas, the little green mung beans and large continental lentils, sometimes called 'green' lentils. Alfalfa and triticale, kinds of wheat, which you can get at health shops, are also excellent, as is ordinary wheat.

To sprout beans or seeds, put four heaped tablespoons of your chosen type into a large (225-g/8-oz) coffee jar, cover with water and leave to stand overnight. Next day cover the top of the jar with a piece of J-cloth or muslin secured with an elastic band. Drain the beans or seeds by pouring out the water through the J-cloth or muslin. Then, again through the cloth or muslin, fill the jar with water from the cold tap, swish it around, and drain it out again. Leave the jar on its side by the draining board. Repeat the rinsing process twice a day. The beans or seeds wil take 2–5 days; they are ready to eat when the shoot is the same length as the bean or seed, except for alfalfa, in which the shoots can get longer, up to about 2cm (1 in). When the sprouts are ready they can be kept in the fridge for several days. Use the whole thing, shoot and seed, for a lovely crunchy salad, or stir-fry.

Avocado, Watercress and Walnut Salad

Although they're expensive, avocados are so nutritious that they're worth serving when you can. This salad is nice for lunch, with wholewheat bread and butter, or on the side, with a dish such as the wholewheat pasta rings in tomato sauce, page 165.

SERVES 2–4

1 tablespoon wine vinegar
3 tablespoons olive oil
salt and pepper
1 large ripe avocado pear

1 large bunch watercress,
  washed
125g (4 oz) walnut pieces

Put the wine vinegar and olive oil into a bowl with some salt and pepper and mix together. Cut the avocado pear in half, remove stone and skin, slice flesh. Put avocado flesh into the bowl and mix gently, then add the watercress and walnuts; serve at once.

Mixed Bean Salad

Serve this with some green salad, such as lettuce or watercress, and warm wholewheat rolls for a main course.

SERVES 4

1 tablespoon wine or cider
  vinegar
3 tablespoons olive oil
½ teaspoon sugar
salt and pepper
300g (10 oz) cooked butter
  beans (see page 135), or a
  425-g (15-oz) can, drained

300g (10 oz) cooked red kidney
  beans (see page 135), or a
  425-g (15-oz) can, drained
2 heaped tablespoons chopped
  parsley
a few spring onions, chopped

Put the wine or cider vinegar into a large bowl or wooden salad bowl with the oil, sugar and some salt and pepper and mix together. Add the beans, parsley and spring onions and stir gently.

To freeze This salad freezes well as long as you're not using beans which have already been frozen. Prepare the salad as above but do not add the parsley and spring onions. Freeze. To use, thaw completely, add chopped parsley and spring onion. Check seasoning.

Beetroot, Orange and Cottage Cheese Salad

SERVES 4

450g (1 lb) cooked beetroot:
  buy this in its skin, from
  the greengrocer
4 large, juicy oranges
1 large bunch watercress,
  washed

350g (12 oz) cottage cheese
2–3 tablespoons sunflower
  seeds, optional

Slip the skins off the beetroot, using your fingers, then rinse the
beetroot under cold water and cut into thin slices. Put into a bowl.
Slice the skin and pith off the oranges by cutting round and round
with a sharp knife, like peeling an apple when you want to keep
the peel whole. Hold the oranges over the bowl of beetroot, to
catch the juice, then slice the oranges into thin rounds. Arrange
watercress, circles of beetroot, circles of orange and cottage cheese
on a large serving dish or individual plates, sprinkle with the
sunflower seeds if you're using them, and serve as soon as possible.

If you don't eat dairy produce Use cooked, drained butter beans
instead of the cottage cheese, or one of the dips on pages 130–4.

Main Course Cabbage Salad

This is a substantial and filling salad, with protein in the form of
the nuts. It makes a complete main course if you serve it with some
wholewheat bread or rolls or a jacket-baked potato. You might
think it would be time-consuming to make, but if you have a good
chopping-board and one of those spring-loaded choppers it can be
done surprisingly quickly – even faster with a food processor, of
course – and can be prepared several hours in advance, because it
will only improve as the cabbage softens in the dressing and
absorbs the flavours.

SERVES 4

1 tablespoon wine or cider
vinegar
2–3 tablespoons olive oil
½ teaspoon sugar
salt and pepper
350g (12 oz) white salad
cabbage
175g (6 oz) carrot, scraped

1 small red or green pepper,
deseeded
small bunch spring onions,
trimmed
50g (2 oz) raisins
100g (4 oz) roasted peanuts (see
page 154), or use salted
ones

Put the wine or cider vinegar into a large bowl or wooden salad
bowl with the oil, sugar and some salt and pepper and mix
together. (Don't add extra salt if you're intending to use salted
peanuts.) Cut the cabbage, carrots and pepper into rough chunks,
then put them all on a board and chop with the autochop. Or put
the whole lot into a food processor and whizz together for a few
seconds. Put chopped vegetables into the bowl with the dressing,
snip in the spring onions, using kitchen scissors, and add the
raisins. Mix everything together. Add the peanuts just before
serving, so that they remain crisp.

Greek Salad

A good salad for the late summer when tomatoes and cucumbers
are cheap. I like this salad with warm, light-textured wholewheat
rolls. The inclusion of the parsley adds extra iron and calcium.

SERVES 4

1 tablespoon wine vinegar
3 tablespoons olive oil
salt and pepper
450g (1 lb) firm tomatoes
1 cucumber
1 large, mild onion

2 heaped tablespoons chopped
parsley, if available
225g (8 oz) firm white cheese:
Cheshire, Caerphilly,
Lancashire or Wensleydale
16 black olives, if liked

Put the vinegar, olive oil and a little seasoning into a large bowl
and mix together to make a dressing. Wash and slice the tomatoes;

cut the cucumber into chunky pieces; slice the onion thinly; cut the cheese into small cubes. Put all these into the bowl with the dressing and turn them gently until evenly coated. Serve piled up attractively on individual dishes.

If you don't eat dairy produce Use cubes of firmed-up tofu (see page 153) instead of the ordinary cheese.

Green Salad

Quicker than doing a cooked vegetable and full of vitamins, green salad is most useful. You can use any green salad vegetables, and the darker they are, the better. Watercress is excellent, also raw spinach and dark green lettuce leaves. Mix a dressing straight into a bowl: I generally use 1 tablespoon wine vinegar and 2–3 tablespoons olive oil, with some salt and pepper. Then simply put in the green vegetables, torn into pieces as necessary, or, in the case of raw spinach, finely shredded. Turn the vegetables gently in the dressing. Chopped fresh herbs, onion and garlic can be added, and the dressing can be made more adventurous with the addition of some mustard and/or a little sugar.

Soya Bean Salad

Soya beans are so nutritious, being rich in iron and thiamine and containing useful amounts of calcium, that it's worth finding a number of different ways of serving them. Here they're mixed with carrots, parsley and spring onions to make a very nourishing salad.

SERVES 4

1 teaspoon barbados molasses
   sugar
1 teaspoon dry mustard
salt
2 tablespoons wine or cider
   vinegar
3 tablespoons oil – olive or
   sunflower

450g (1 lb) cooked soya beans
   – see page 135
3 large carrots, coarsely grated
small bunch spring onions,
   trimmed and chopped
2 heaped tablespoons chopped
   parsley

Put the sugar and mustard into a bowl with a little salt and mix
to a paste with the vinegar. Then gradually add the oil. Stir in the
soya beans, carrots, spring onions and parsley. Taste, and add a
little more salt if necessary. A few drops of Shoyu soy sauce (from
health shops) are nice in this, too.

Spinach Salad

Uncooked spinach is an excellent source of iron, vitamin C and
folic acid, and this is one of my favourite salads for which I get
cravings if I'm a bit tired or run down. It can be served as a side
salad, though I prefer it on its own, as a cleansing lunch or supper.
You could add some sprouted seeds (page 121) or scatter some
pumpkin seeds, sesame seeds or the savoury seed mix on page 171
on top for protein, if you like.

SERVES 4

1 tablespoon wine vinegar
2–3 tablespoons olive oil
450g (1 lb) spinach, washed and
   shredded as finely as
   possible
salt and pepper

2 leeks, about 300g (10 oz)
   together, washed, trimmed
   and finely shredded – use as
   much of the green part as is
   reasonably tender

Put the vinegar and oil into a salad bowl and mix together. Add
the spinach and leeks and mix gently. Season with salt and pepper
and serve at once. Add a few drops of Shoyu soy sauce (from health
shops) if you like.

Grated Swede Salad

A delicious, creamy salad that's rich in B vitamins.

SERVES 4

450g (1 lb) grated raw swede
2 heaped tablespoons
  mayonnaise
3 heaped tablespoons natural
  yoghurt
salt and pepper

bunch watercress, washed and
  trimmed
4 tomatoes, sliced
125g (4 oz) home-grown
  sprouted mung beans, if
  available

Mix together the swede, mayonnaise and yoghurt. Season with salt and pepper; spoon into a large dish. Tuck the watercress all round the edge of the swede, then arrange the tomato slices on top and finally sprinkle with the sprouted beans.

If you don't eat dairy produce Use an eggless mayonnaise, such as the one made by Flora.

Tabbouleh

A useful salad, because it's a good way of eating a lot of parsley, which is a very good source of both calcium and iron. Serve as a main salad course, with some crisp lettuce leaves on the side and perhaps some yoghurt dressing (page 119).

SERVES 4

225g (8 oz) bulgur wheat –
  from health shops
600ml (1 pint) boiling water
3 tablespoons olive oil
1 tablespoon lemon juice
225g (8 oz) chopped parsley

2 tomatoes, skinned and finely
  chopped
2 tablespoons chopped mint
salt and pepper
extra olive oil to serve,
  optional

Put the wheat into a bowl, cover with the boiling water and leave to soak for 15 minutes. After this the wheat will probably have absorbed the water; if not, drain off the excess. Add the oil, lemon juice, parsley, tomatoes and mint to the wheat, and salt and pepper to taste. Mix well. Spoon salad on to a shallow serving dish, level top and press down to make a flat, cake-like shape. Chill. Spoon a little olive oil on top before serving, if liked.

Not suitable for freezing

Vitality Salad Bowl

This is pleasant spooned into a warm pitta bread pocket and topped with some mayonnaise or tofu dressing and a sprinkling of cress.

SERVES 4

1 tablespoon wine or cider
  vinegar
1 tablespoon olive oil
salt and pepper
1 tablespoon lemon juice
125g (4 oz) wheat sprouts or
  wholewheat grains, soaked
  overnight then cooked for
  1¼ hours or 25 minutes in a
  pressure cooker

225g (8 oz) home-grown bean
  sprouts
2 carrots, coarsely grated
50g (2 oz) raisins
4 tomatoes, diced
10cm (4 in) cucumber, diced
2 sticks celery, sliced

Put the vinegar and oil into a bowl with some salt and pepper and mix together. Then add the wheat, bean sprouts, carrots, raisins, tomatoes and cucumber, and turn gently so that they all get coated with the dressing.

Not suitable for freezing

Packed Meals

As I explained on page 48, it's a good idea to take some sandwiches with you when you go into hospital: the average hospital doesn't provide food for visitors, especially at 3 a.m., and your partner will need to keep his strength up! So here are some ideas for sandwiches, including ones which can be made in advance and kept in the freezer until required. If you're going to store them in the freezer, use fresh ingredients (not from the freezer) for the outside and the fillings. Use wholewheat bread, rolls or pitta bread, the treacle scones on page 201, or the bran, apricot and almond fruit bread on page 193. Butter lightly and spread with your choice of fillings, avoiding salad ingredients and hardboiled eggs which do not freeze well. Sandwiches will keep in the freezer for 3–4 weeks.

Add some crunchy bars, page 202, or one of the cakes on pages 193–200 and some fresh fruit to complete the meal.

Here are some ideas:

SWEET

Clear honey mixed with finely grated nuts
Curd cheese with chopped crystallized ginger
Curd cheese with chopped 'canned in its own juice' pineapple
125g (4 oz) dates softened by heating in 5 tablespoons water then
    beaten smooth
Dates softened as above with chopped nuts added, or some curd
    cheese beaten in peanut butter and sliced banana (don't freeze)

SAVOURY

Slice of cold nut savoury (page 143 or 147) with chutney
Hazel nut and vegetable pasties (page 144)
Soya sausage (page 149) with pickle in a soft wholewheat roll
Grated cheese or vegan cheese with pickle
Any of the dips or spreads below
Cooked beans in a little oil and vinegar dressing (page 122)
Soya bean salad (page 125) in a pocket of pitta bread
Peanut butter with finely grated carrot (don't freeze)
Peanut butter with sliced cucumber (don't freeze)
Cabbage salad (page 123) in a pocket of pitta bread (don't freeze)
Vitality salad (page 128) in a pocket of pitta bread (don't freeze)
Greek salad (page 124) in a pocket of pitta bread (don't freeze)
Cooked chickpeas or soya beans with grated carrot and spring onion, mixed with some mayonnaise or tofu dressing (page 120) in pitta bread (don't freeze)

DIPS AND SPREADS

Bean Spread

MAKES ABOUT 350G (12 OZ)

300g (10 oz) cooked butter
  beans (page 135) or a 425-g
  (15-oz) can
1 garlic clove, crushed
1 tablespoon olive oil

2 teaspoons wine vinegar
a few drops of Tabasco sauce
  or a pinch of cayenne
salt and pepper

Drain the beans, keeping the liquid. Mash the beans and add the garlic, olive oil, vinegar and enough of the reserved cooking liquid to make a consistency like softly whipped cream. Alternatively, blend ingredients in liquidizer or food processor. Add a drop or two of Tabasco or a pinch of cayenne and salt and pepper. Spoon into a small container.

To freeze Leave out the garlic and Tabasco or cayenne. Put spread into small container, cover and freeze. Remove from freezer 2 hours in advance. Garlic and Tabasco or cayenne can be added before use.

Hummus

MAKES ABOUT 350G (12 OZ)

300g (10 oz) cooked chickpeas
   (page 135), or a 425-g
   (15-oz) can
1 garlic clove, crushed

2 tablespoons olive oil
1 tablespoon lemon juice
salt and pepper

Make in the same way as the bean spread above, adding the lemon juice with the oil and beating in enough cooking liquid to make a soft consistency. Strictly speaking, some tahini, or sesame cream, should be added to hummus, but over the years I find I've decreased the quantity steadily and now I generally leave this out! But you could beat in up to two tablespoons of tahini to taste, if you like, which will also increase the nutritional value of this dish considerably, since tahini is an excellent source of calcium.

To freeze As for bean spread, above.

Cheese Spread

MAKES ABOUT 200G (7 OZ)

40g (1½ oz) polyunsaturated
   margarine
150g (5 oz) grated cheese
6 tablespoons milk

pinch cayenne pepper or a few
   drops Tabasco sauce
salt and pepper

Put all the ingredients into a food processor and blend to a creamy consistency. Or put margarine into a bowl and beat until soft, then gradually beat in cheese and milk. Season with a pinch of cayenne or a few drops of Tabasco and some salt and pepper. Spoon into a small dish or other container. Use on unbuttered bread.

If you don't eat dairy produce Use homemade vegan cheese (page 133) and soya milk, and omit margarine.

To freeze Cover dish with polythene, freeze. Remove from freezer 2 hours before required.

Curried Soya Bean and Apple Spread

MAKES ABOUT 500G (1 LB 2 OZ)

1 small onion, finely chopped	1 tablespoon curry powder
15g (½ oz) polyunsaturated margarine	300g (10 oz) cooked soya beans (page 135)
125g (4 oz) peeled and cored cooking apple, finely chopped	salt and pepper

Fry the onion in the margarine for 5 minutes, then add the apple and curry powder, and fry, covered, for a further 5 minutes, until onion and apple are soft. Remove from heat and add soya beans. Mash well, adding a little water if necessary to make a soft consistency (use the water in which the beans were cooked, if you have it). Spoon mixture into a small container.

To freeze Not ideal for freezing because of the curry powder, which can develop a musty flavour, but if you want to risk it, freeze as for bean spread (page 130), for not more than 3–4 weeks.

Hazel Nut Spread

MAKES ABOUT 225G (8 OZ)

100g (4 oz) hazel nuts	1 garlic clove, crushed
100g (4 oz) sunflower seeds	1 tablespoon Shoyu soy sauce, from health shops
15g (½ oz) polyunsaturated margarine	salt and pepper
4 tablespoons hot water	

Toast nuts and sunflower seeds under a hot grill or in a moderate oven until golden brown. If nuts still have brown skins on, remove these after toasting by rubbing nuts gently in a soft, clean cloth. Grind nuts and sunflower seeds finely in a coffee grinder or blender. Mix nuts and sunflower seeds with the margarine, water, garlic and soy sauce. Beat until smooth and creamy. Season with salt and pepper. Spoon into a small dish.

Homemade Peanut Butter

Peanut butter is nutritious and many babies love it. However, since some of the commercial ones are rather salty, you might like to make your own, which is quite easy to do if you've got an electric coffee grinder, liquidizer or food processor.

MAKES ABOUT 225G (8 OZ)

200g (7 oz) peanuts, roasted as described on page 154, and the skins rubbed off in a soft cloth

ground nut oil (or corn oil or sunflower oil), preferably cold-pressed (from health shops)

Grind the peanuts to a powder: be careful that no large pieces remain. Put the peanut powder into a bowl and add enough oil to make a spreading consistency. Keep mixture in a jar in the fridge. It will keep in the fridge for several weeks, but will separate, the oil coming to the top, since it naturally contains no emulsifiers or stabilizer; simply stir the oil into the solid part before use.

Vegan Cheese

MAKES ABOUT 225G (8 OZ)

125g (4 oz) hard vegetable margarine such as Tomor, or Suenut, both from health shops

1 teaspoon yeast extract or miso
125g (4 oz) soya flour
salt and pepper

Put the margarine or Suenut and yeast extract or miso into a saucepan and heat until melted. Remove from heat and stir in the soya flour and seasoning to taste. Pour mixture into a small dish or suitable mould such as a small polythene container. Cool, then chill until firm. Can be sliced or grated and used as a replacement for dairy cheese.

To freeze Cover dish with polythene, freeze. Remove from freezer 2 hours before required.

Peanut or Almond Spread

MAKES ABOUT 225G (8 OZ)

25g (1 oz) hard vegetable margarine such as Tomor, or Suenut, both from health shops
1 teaspoon yeast extract
125g (4 oz) peanuts, toasted under a grill, or in the oven as described for hazel nut spread (page 132), or 225g (8 oz) almonds

1 tablespoon lemon juice
1 tablespoon Shoyu soy sauce
dash of Tabasco sauce
salt and pepper

Put the margarine or Suenut and yeast extract into a saucepan and heat until melted. Remove from heat. Grind nuts finely in a coffee mill or blender and add to melted margarine. Add lemon juice, soy sauce, a drop or two of Tabasco and salt and pepper. Pour mixture into a small dish or suitable mould, such as a small polythene container. Cool, then chill until firm. Use on unbuttered bread.

To freeze Cover dish with polythene, freeze. Remove from freezer 2 hours before required.

Freezer Dishes

The more meals you can get into the freezer before the baby is born, the better. As well as the dishes in this section, all of which freeze well, it's helpful to have some of the following 'freezer basics' for making vegetarian meals quickly and easily.

Cooked pulses A supply of your favourite varieties, frozen in convenient quantities, is most useful and saves having to rely on cans when you're in a hurry. Varieties which I find particularly useful are red kidney beans, butter beans, chickpeas and soya beans. Prepare a bag (500g/1 lb 2 oz) at a time: wash the beans, then soak for 6–8 hours in cold water. Drain the beans into a colander and rinse under the cold tap. Then put the beans into a pan with fresh cold water. Sometimes, especially with soya beans, I add 6–8 bay leaves. Bring to the boil and boil hard for 10 minutes, then simmer gently until tender – about 1 hour for red kidney beans and butter beans, 2–3 hours for chickpeas and 3 hours for soya beans.

You can save time and heat by using a pressure cooker. Until recently, I've had reservations about using a pressure cooker for pulses because of their tendency to froth up and block the valve. So I'm very grateful to the lady who came to one of my cookery demonstrations and told me this simple and foolproof method. Place the trivet in the base of the pressure cooker and put the beans into the metal baskets or containers. Add only 300ml (10 fl oz) water for the quick-cooking beans, 600ml (1 pint) for soya beans and chickpeas. Bring to pressure and cook for 15 minutes, or 1 hour for soya beans and chickpeas.

Whichever cooking method you use, drain the beans and divide into five 300-g (10-oz) portions – these portions are equivalent to a 425-g (15-oz) can. Pack in suitable containers – I generally put mine into small polythene bags, then gather all these into another, larger one, to keep them together. Label and freeze. Though it's best to thaw these before use, they can be used straight from the freezer if you put them into a colander and rinse under hot water to separate them.

Wholewheat breadcrumbs Very convenient as an addition to nut roasts and savoury bakes, for topping *au gratin* dishes and coating rissoles. Remove crusts from slices of bread, break into pieces and whizz to crumbs in food processor or blender. The bread needs to be on the stale side: I generally use up odd crusts and bits and pieces from the bread bin as they accumulate. Freeze in a polythene bag and take out as required.

For dried breadcrumbs, spread fresh crumbs in a thin layer on a dry baking sheet. Bake at 190°C (375°F), gs mark 5, for about 10 minutes, until golden brown. Store in the freezer or in an airtight jar.

Chopped parsley I find a bag of chopped parsley very useful indeed. Wash parsley well, remove stalks, chop – this can be done speedily in a food processor – and store in a polythene bag.

White sauce Although this can be made fairly quickly, it saves time and effort if you have some in the freezer, for serving with nut savouries and for adding to cooked vegetables and pulses for *au gratin* dishes. Make up according to recipe on page 138; freeze in 300-ml (½-pint) containers.

Tomato sauce Another indispensable basic. Follow recipe on page 139; freeze in 300-ml (½-pint) containers.

Vegetarian gravy If you like gravy with nut savouries, it's worth making up an extra-large batch and freezing in 300-ml (½-pint) containers, or smaller one-person portions if, say, only one person in the family likes gravy.

Wholewheat flan cases Although a wholewheat flan can be made quickly, again, it's handy to have some ready-baked ones in the freezer. They can be used straight from the freezer and quickly filled with an easy egg-and-cheese mixture, or vegetables in a white or cheese sauce, then baked.

Made-up dishes The most useful dishes to make for the freezer are ones which are complete in themselves (or with a sauce which you freeze with them) and need only a simple vegetable or salad to accompany them. Casserole dishes, vegetable and nut or pulse pies with potato or pastry toppings are examples. Nut roasts are useful, either frozen whole or in slices for using as required: in either case, it's especially helpful if you also freeze some sauce for serving with them.

SAUCES FOR THE FREEZER

Vegetarian Gravy

MAKES ABOUT 900ML (JUST OVER 1½ PINT)

1 onion, peeled and chopped	1 vegetable stock cube,
3 tablespoons oil	optional
50g (2 oz) flour – I use 85 per	2 teaspoons yeast extract
cent wholewheat	1 tablespoon Shoyu soy sauce,
1 garlic clove, crushed	from health shops
850ml (1½ pint) water	salt and pepper

Fry the onion in the oil for 10 minutes. Add the flour, and let it brown over the heat, stirring all the time. Then put in all the remaining ingredients. Bring to the boil and leave to simmer for 10 minutes. Then strain and season to taste. If you like bits of onion in your gravy, there's no need to strain, of course, and in this case you could use a 100 per cent flour instead of the one suggested. (There's no point in using the 100 per cent flour if you're going to strain the gravy, because the bran will get left in the sieve anyway.)

White Sauce and Variations

These ingredients double up satisfactorily if you want to make a larger quantity but you'll need a big saucepan. I like to use unbleached white flour from the health shop as it's free from chemicals and additives, but ordinary plain flour would also do.

MAKES ABOUT 600ML (1 PINT)

50g (2 oz) butter or polyunsaturated margarine
50g (2 oz) unbleached white flour
600ml (1 pint) milk or soya milk
1 bay leaf
salt and pepper

For the traditional method, melt butter or margarine then stir in flour. Cook for 1 minute, then add a third of the milk and stir until thickened; repeat with another third, then finally add the rest, together with bay leaf and seasoning. Or, put all ingredients into pan and whisk together over moderate heat until thickened. Or, liquidize butter or margarine, flour and milk for 1 minute, then pour into pan and stir over moderate heat until thickened. In all cases, simmer gently for 10 minutes, to cook the flour, then season.

Variations

Parsley sauce
Add 2 heaped tablespoons chopped parsley (or more – parsley is a wonderful source of calcium and iron) to the cooked sauce.

Cheese sauce
Stir 50–100g (2–4 oz) grated cheese and a pinch of dry mustard powder or cayenne pepper into cooked sauce.

To freeze Pour sauce into suitable container, allowing enough room for the sauce to expand as it freezes. To use, remove from freezer and allow to thaw for about 2 hours. Stir gently over heat.

Tomato Sauce

MAKES ABOUT 350ML (12 FL OZ)

1 onion, peeled and chopped
2 tablespoons oil
1 425-g (15-oz) can tomatoes
salt and pepper

Fry onion in oil for 10 minutes, until soft, then remove from heat, add tomatoes and liquidize – no further cooking is needed. Season with salt and pepper.

To freeze Pour into suitable container, allowing room for sauce to expand as it freezes. To use, allow up to 2 hours for sauce to defreeze.

FREEZER SAVOURIES

Buckwheat Bake

Like the other grains, buckwheat is rich in iron and B vitamins. It also contains a substance called rutin which naturopaths prescribe for high blood pressure and varicose veins, so it could be a useful grain to use if you're suffering from these. Serve with a lettuce or watercress salad.

SERVES 4

175g (6 oz) toasted buckwheat: buy this, already toasted, from the health shop

400ml (¾ pint) hot water

1 teaspoon yeast extract

salt

15g (½ oz) butter or margarine

1 large onion, peeled and chopped

3 carrots, scraped and sliced

2 leeks, washed and sliced

125g (4 oz) button mushrooms, washed and sliced

225g (8 oz) tomatoes, skinned and sliced

pepper

For topping

1 tablespoon plain, wholewheat flour

300ml (10 fl oz) natural yoghurt

1 egg

If you're going to serve this immediately, set oven to 190°C (375°F), gas mark 5: there's no need to do this if you're cooking for the freezer. Grease a shallow ovenproof dish. Put the buckwheat into a saucepan with the hot water, yeast extract and a little salt; bring back to the boil, stir, then put a lid on the saucepan, turn the heat right down and leave to cook for 10 minutes, until the buckwheat is fluffy and all the water absorbed. Meanwhile, melt the butter or margarine in a saucepan and fry the onion, carrot and leek gently, with a lid on the pan, for 7 minutes. Add the mushrooms and tomatoes and cook for a further 3 minutes. Season. Put half the buckwheat into the casserole dish, spoon the vegetables over and top with the rest of the buckwheat.

If you don't eat dairy produce Omit egg; use vegan yoghurt (see page 191) and 2 tablespoons flour for topping.

To use immediately Whisk together the flour, yoghurt and egg. Season and pour over the top of the bake. Bake for 30 minutes.

To freeze Cool bake, freeze. Thaw for 3–4 hours; cover with topping and bake as above.

Butter Bean and Vegetable Casserole

Serve this with baked potatoes or some cooked brown rice or buckwheat (see page 139).

SERVES 4–6

2 large onions
2 tablespoons oil
900g (2 lb) mixed root
   vegetables – carrot, swede,
   parsnip, turnip, celery, as
   available, cut into even-sized
   pieces
2 tablespoons 85 per cent
   flour

175g (6 oz) butter beans, soaked
   for 6–8 hours in cold water,
   then drained and rinsed
900ml (1½ pint) water
2 vegetable stock cubes
1–2 tablespoons Shoyu soy
   sauce, from health shops
salt and pepper
chopped parsley

Fry the onion in the oil for 5 minutes, then add the vegetables and stir for a minute or two. Sprinkle in the flour and mix with the vegetables, then add the butter beans, water and stock cubes. Simmer gently for 1–1½ hours, stirring occasionally, until vegetables and beans are tender, or bake at 160°C (325°F), gas mark 3, for 1½ hours. Add soy sauce and season to taste.

To use immediately Sprinkle with chopped parsley.

To freeze Cook as above, undercooking vegetables and beans slightly. Cool quickly. Put into a rigid container allowing enough room for expansion. To use, remove from freezer and allow to defreeze for 6 hours or overnight. Transfer to saucepan, stir over a gentle heat, or bake as described above for 30–40 minutes, until heated through.

Carrot Slices

These freeze well and are pleasant with parsley sauce and vegetables or a salad. They also contain oats, which are a useful traditional remedy for 'baby blues'.

SERVES 4

150g (5 oz) rolled oats
175g (6 oz) finely grated
  carrot
175g (6 oz) grated cheese

1 egg, beaten
1 teaspoon mixed herbs
salt and pepper
a little margarine

Grease a 20×30cm (7¾×12in) swiss roll tin. Put oats, carrot, cheese, egg and herbs into a bowl and mix together. Season, then press into tin, and dot with margarine.

If you don't eat dairy produce Use vegan cheese (page 133) instead of dairy cheese, and 1 tablespoon soya flour mixed with 3 tablespoons water instead of egg.

To use immediately Bake for about 25–30 minutes, at 190°C (375°F), gas mark 5, until set and lightly browned.

To freeze Bake for 10 minutes at 190°C (375°F), gas mark 5, cool, freeze. To use, allow to thaw for 2–3 hours, then bake for 15–20 minutes.

Chunky Nut and Vegetable Roast

This nut roast has a pleasant, chewy texture. If you're making it for a baby to share, however, it would be better to grind the nuts and chop the vegetables more finely.

SERVES 4–6

1 carrot, scraped
1 onion, peeled
1 celery stick
225g (8 oz) mixed nuts: for instance, almonds, peanuts, brazil nuts
2 teaspoons yeast extract

2 eggs
1–2 teaspoons dried mixed herbs
salt and pepper
butter and dried crumbs (see page 136) for coating tin

Set oven to 190°C (375°F), gas mark 5. Put all the ingredients into a food processor and process until vegetables and nuts are chopped into chunky pieces. Or spread the vegetables and nuts out on a large board and chop with an autochop, then put into a bowl and mix with the remaining ingredients. Line a 450-g (1-lb) loaf tin with a strip of non-stick paper. Grease well and sprinkle with dry crumbs. Spoon nut mixture into tin, level top. Bake uncovered for 45 minutes, until centre is set.

If you don't eat dairy produce Replace eggs with 2 tablespoons wholewheat flour and mix well.

To use immediately Slip a knife round the edge and turn loaf out on to a warm serving dish. It's good with vegetarian gravy (page 137) and cooked vegetables, or cold with yoghurt dressing (page 119) and salad.

To freeze Bake for 20 minutes, cool quickly, freeze. To use, allow to thaw for 3–4 hours, then bake for 25–30 minutes.

Hazel Nut and Vegetable Pasties

These are particularly useful as a lunch-box item; other nuts can be used instead of the hazel nuts – roasted peanuts are good. If you're making this for the baby to share, finely grind the nuts and keep back some of the filling for the baby when making the pasties (the baby doesn't need pastry).

MAKES 4

1 onion, peeled and chopped
2 tablespoons oil
225g (8 oz) potato, peeled and cut into 6-mm (¼-in) dice
225g (8 oz) carrot, scraped and cut into 6-mm (¼-in) dice
1 tablespoon tomato purée
1 teaspoon basil
125g (4 oz) skinned hazel nuts, chopped

salt and pepper
200g (8 oz) wholewheat pastry made from 200g (8 oz) 100 per cent wholewheat flour, 100g (4 oz) vegetable margarine and 3 tablespoons cold water

Fry the onion in the oil for 5 minutes, then add the potato and carrots. Cover and cook gently for 10–15 minutes, until vegetables are just tender, stirring often. Add tomato purée, basil and hazel nuts; season to taste. Leave on one side to cool while you make the pastry. Set oven to 200°C (400°F), gas mark 6. Divide pastry into 4 pieces, roll each into a circle 15cm (6 in) across. Spoon a quarter of the vegetable mixture on to the centre, fold up pastry and press together edges, like a Cornish pasty. Make steam-holes, bake for 20–25 minutes.

To freeze Can be frozen before or after cooking. If freezing before cooking don't make steam-holes, as liquid will expand and flow out of these. To use, defreeze for 3–4 hours. Baked pasties can be used straight away or heated through gently for about 10 minutes in a moderate oven. For unbaked pasties, make steam-holes, then bake as described above.

Leek and Potato Pie

In the summer this can also be made with courgettes, sliced and very lightly cooked in a little boiling water until just tender.

SERVES 4

750g (1½ lb) potatoes, peeled and cut into even-sized chunks

750g (1½ lb) leeks, trimmed, washed and sliced

50g (2 oz) butter or polyunsaturated margarine

50g (2 oz) unbleached white flour

600ml (1 pint) milk or soya milk

2 heaped tablespoons chopped parsley

50g (2 oz) grated cheese

salt and pepper

Set oven to 200°C (400°F), gas mark 6. Boil potatoes in water to cover until tender, then drain and mash with 15g (½ oz) of the butter or margarine and 150ml (¼ pint) of the milk; season to taste. Boil leeks in 2cm (1 in) lightly salted water for 5–7 minutes, until tender. Drain well. While vegetables are cooking, make the sauce: put remaining butter or margarine into a saucepan with the flour and milk and whisk together over moderate heat until thickened, then simmer gently for 10 minutes. Add drained leeks and parsley and season to taste. Spoon this mixture into a shallow ovenproof dish and spread mashed potato evenly over the top. Sprinkle with remaining cheese.

If you don't eat dairy produce Use homemade vegan cheese (page 133) instead of dairy cheese.

To use immediately Bake for 40 minutes.

To freeze Freeze pie before baking. To use, allow to defrost for 5–6 hours, or overnight, then bake as above.

Lentil and Onion Cutlets

Lentils are an excellent source of iron. This recipe makes a large batch of cutlets for the freezer.

MAKES 20

500g (1 lb) split red lentils	4 tablespoons oil
850ml (1½ pints) water	3–4 tablespoons lemon juice
4 bay leaves	salt and pepper
3 large onions, peeled and finely chopped	wholewheat flour for coating
	oil for shallow-frying

Put the lentils into a pan with water and bay leaves. Bring to the boil, then cover and turn the heat right down. Cook very gently for 15–20 minutes, until lentils are soft and pale coloured. Meanwhile, fry the onions in the oil for 10 minutes, until softened. Add the onions and mix well, mashing the lentils as you do so. Then add the lemon juice and salt and pepper to taste. Form into cutlet shapes – don't make them too big if you want to use them straight from the freezer – and coat with wholewheat flour.

To use immediately Shallow-fry in a little oil, treating them gently, as they're rather fragile. They're good with the yoghurt dressing on page 119 and a salad, or gravy, mint sauce and cooked vegetables.

To freeze Put the cutlets on a large plate or baking tray and freeze, uncovered, until solid. Then put them into a polythene bag or container. They can be used from frozen as long as you cook them gently to allow time for the centre to cook through. Or allow to thaw for about 2 hours, then fry.

Mixed Nut Roast

SERVES 4

butter and dried crumbs (see page 136) for coating tin
1 large onion, peeled and chopped
3 tablespoons oil
1 heaped tablespoon wholewheat flour
150ml (5 fl oz) milk or water
1 teaspoon yeast extract
1 heaped teaspoon mixed herbs

125g (4 oz) wholewheat breadcrumbs
225g (8 oz) finely grated mixed nuts: use a selection of almonds, brazil nuts, walnuts, roasted peanuts, hazel nuts, cashew nuts, as available
salt and pepper

Set oven to 180°C (350°F), gas mark 4. Grease a loaf tin with butter and line base and short narrow sides with a piece of well-buttered, non-stick paper; sprinkle with dried crumbs. Fry the onion in the oil for 10 minutes, browning lightly. Add the flour, stir for a minute, then pour in the water and stir over the heat until very thick. Remove from the heat and add the rest of the ingredients. Season with salt and pepper. Spoon mixture into prepared tin, press down. Bake for 45 minutes, until firm in the centre.

To use immediately Slip a knife round the edge and turn loaf out on to a warm serving dish. It's good with vegetarian gravy (page 137) and redcurrant or cranberry jelly, or cold with yoghurt dressing (page 119) and salad.

To freeze Bake for 20 minutes, cool quickly, freeze. To use, allow to thaw for 3–4 hours, then bake for 25–30 minutes.

Rice, Tomato and Cashew Nut Bake

This dish can be served with extra tomato sauce (page 139) and a cooked green vegetable, or just a green salad.

SERVES 4

175g (6 oz) brown rice
salt
1 onion, peeled and chopped
2 tablespoons oil
1 425-g (15-oz) can tomatoes
grated rind and juice of ½
  lemon

1 tablespoon chopped parsley
125g (4 oz) finely chopped or
  grated cashew nuts
pepper
wholewheat crumbs and a little
  butter for topping

Put the rice into a medium-sized saucepan with 400 ml (¾ pint) water and ½ teaspoon salt. Bring to the boil, then cover, turn heat right down and leave to cook for 45 minutes. While rice is cooking, fry the onion in the oil for 10 minutes, then add the tomatoes, lemon juice and parsley and remove from the heat. Add this mixture to the cooked rice together with the cashew nuts and fork through. Season with salt and pepper. Turn mixture into a greased, shallow, ovenproof dish and sprinkle crumbs over the top. Dot with butter.

To use immediately Bake at 200°C (400°F), gas mark 6, for about 30 minutes, until top is crisp.

To freeze Freeze before baking. To use, allow to defrost for 5–6 hours, then bake as above.

Soya Sausages

These sausages are far more nutritious than meat ones, since the soya and peanuts provide B vitamins, iron, calcium and other valuable minerals. If you like this recipe, it would probably be worth making up a larger quantity: use 500g (1 lb 2 oz) soya beans, 450g (1 lb) peanuts and multiply the rest of the ingredients by five.

SERVES 4

1 onion, peeled and finely
  chopped
2 tablespoons oil
1 garlic clove, crushed
300g (10 oz) cooked soya beans
  (see page 135)
100g (3½ oz) grated roasted
  peanuts (see page 154)

1 tablespoon Shoyu soy sauce,
  from health shops
1 tablespoon tomato purée
1 tablespoon lemon juice
1 teaspoon mixed herbs
salt and pepper
wholewheat flour for coating
oil for shallow-frying

Fry the onion in the oil for 10 minutes, browning lightly, then add the remaining ingredients, mashing everything together to make a paste. Form into sausage shapes, coat with wholewheat flour.

To use immediately Shallow-fry in hot oil, turning the sausages so that they get crisp all over. Drain on kitchen paper.

To freeze Spread sausage on a plate or baking tray and freeze uncovered until solid. Transfer to container. They can be used from frozen as long as you fry them slowly to allow them to cook right through. Or thaw, then fry in the usual way.

Soya and Walnut Loaf

SERVES 4

butter and dried crumbs (see
  page 136) for coating tin
1 onion, peeled and finely
  chopped
2 sticks of celery, finely
  chopped
2 tablespoons oil
300g (10 oz) cooked soya beans
  (see page 135)

100g (3½ oz) chopped
  walnuts
2 tomatoes, skinned and
  chopped
1 tablespoon tomato purée
1 tablespoon lemon juice
1 teaspoon mixed herbs
2 eggs
salt and pepper

Grease a 450-g (1-lb) loaf tin with butter and line base and short narrow sides with a piece of well-buttered, non-stick paper; sprinkle with dried crumbs. Fry the onion and celery in the oil for 10 minutes, browning lightly. Remove from the heat and mix with the soya beans, walnuts, tomatoes, tomato purée, lemon juice, herbs, eggs, and seasoning to taste. Mix well, mashing the soya beans a bit to help bind mixture together. Spoon into prepared tin, press down well.

If you don't eat dairy produce Replace eggs with 2 tablespoons wholewheat flour and mix well.

To use immediately Bake for 45 minutes at 180°C (350°F), gas mark 4, until firm in the centre. Slip a knife round the edge and turn loaf out on to a warm serving dish. It's good with vegetarian gravy (page 137) or parsley sauce (page 138) and cooked vegetables, or cold with pickles, and it makes a good filling for a soft wholewheat bap or pitta bread.

To freeze Bake for 20 minutes, at 180°C (350°F), gas mark 4, cool quickly, freeze. To use, allow to thaw for 3–4 hours, then bake for 25–30 minutes.

Vegetable and Butter Bean Pie

SERVES 4

1 large onion, peeled and
   chopped
3 tablespoons oil
2 teaspoons unbleached flour
300ml (½ pint) water
1 teaspoon yeast extract
1 carrot, scraped and diced
1 stick of celery, chopped
1 leek, trimmed, cleaned and
   sliced
125g (4 oz) button mushrooms,
   sliced

1 tomato, peeled and chopped
1 425-g (15-oz) can butter
   beans, or home-cooked beans
   (see page 135), drained
200g (8 oz) wholewheat pastry
   made from 200g (8 oz) 100
   per cent wholewheat flour,
   100g (4 oz) vegetable
   margarine and 3 tablespoons
   cold water

Fry the onion in the oil for 10 minutes, then stir in the flour and allow to brown over the heat. Pour in the water and add the yeast extract; stir until thickened, season. Add the carrot, celery and leek; cover, then simmer over a gentle heat for about 15 minutes, until vegetables are cooked. Remove from heat and add mushrooms, tomatoes and butter beans. Cool, while you make the pastry. Pour the vegetable mixture into a pie dish. Put an upturned egg cup or pie funnel in the centre of the dish to support the pastry. Roll out the pastry rather thickly to fit the top of the dish. Cut 1-cm (½-in) wide strips from the trimmings; brush with cold water, place on rim of pie dish, press down, brush with more cold water. Put pastry on top of pie, trim. Make two steam-holes.

To use immediately Bake for 20 minutes, at 220°C (425°F), gas mark 7, then reduce oven setting to 200°C (400°F), gas mark 6, and bake for a further 20 minutes.

To freeze This pie can be frozen before or after cooking. If freezing before cooking don't make steam-holes, as liquid will expand and flow out of these. To use, defreeze for 6–8 hours, make steam-holes if necessary. Bake uncooked pie as described above; cover cooked pie with foil and heat through in a moderate oven (180°C/350°F), gas mark 4) for 20–30 minutes.

Quick Main Meals

However well stocked your deepfreeze, you'll also need a repertoire of healthy dishes which need the minimum of preparation, for using before the baby is born, when you're tired, and after the baby is born, when you're tired and hectic! It's quite true that on the whole it's more effort to make wholefood/vegetarian dishes than to put together a meal using convenience foods. But there are some wholefood ingredients which are very easy to use, and when these are combined with fresh vegetables which require the minimum of preparation, the result is a quick meal which is also healthy and tasty. The recipes which follow are all examples of this.

First, a note on the ingredients used.

Store cupboard for quick meals

Eggs If you eat dairy produce, eggs are a great natural convenience food; scrambled eggs on wholewheat toast, or an omelette with a buttery flavour and creamy inside, make soothing and welcoming quick meals. Hardboiled eggs are a useful way of adding protein to a rice or vegetable dish, or can be combined with a cheese or parsley sauce to make a main dish in their own right.

Cheese Again, for vegetarians eating dairy produce, cheese is a useful stand-by for quick meals, and it's worth grating a good quantity to keep in the fridge and have ready when you need it quickly. Vegan cheese, made from soya flour (page 133), can be used similarly: it's worth making up a good quantity and keeping some in the freezer. Toasted cheese – grated cheese heaped on top of unbuttered wholewheat toast and melted under a hot grill – makes an almost instant supper and is delicious with watercress or a sliced tomato and spring onion salad, which can be quickly made while the cheese is melting. Cooked, easy-to-prepare vegetables such as cauliflower can be placed in a shallow ovenproof dish, sprinkled with grated cheese and grilled to make a protein-rich main dish (see page 172); and grated cheese will turn jacket-baked or mashed potatoes into a main course (for other, non-dairy toppings for jacket potatoes, see page 175).

Cereals: brown rice, millet, bulgur (or burghul) wheat These are all extremely easy to prepare – see pages 156–63 – and form a good basis for a main dish, or turn a vegetable mixture such as ratatouille or even just a good homemade tomato or curry sauce, into a complete meal. Cereals are a good source of protein but can be made even better by adding small quantities of grated or cubed cheese, chopped hardboiled egg, nuts, sunflower or sesame seeds or cooked red beans, chickpeas or butter beans. The mixture can be made tasty by adding some of the more quickly prepared vegetables, perhaps fried with some spices, before serving.

Pulses: butter beans, red kidney beans, chickpeas Cans of these – or a supply of your own cooked beans in your freezer, frozen in convenient quantities, as described on page 135 – are very useful for quick meals. Look for beans canned in just salt and water, without other additives if possible, and add to vegetable stews (see page 180), fork into cooked brown rice, coat with a simple oil and vinegar dressing for a filling salad, or mix with a tasty sauce and serve with rice or millet, potato, crisp wholewheat toast or just a simple salad.

Also in this category, since it's made from soya, is tofu, a nutritious bean curd which has been used in China for centuries. It looks rather like junket and has a bland flavour. It's not as cheap as ordinary pulses, but is concentrated and nutritious. For some recipes it needs firming up. To do this, drain the tofu, then wrap it in several layers of clean absorbent cloth, place in a colander, put a weight on top and leave for at least 1 hour, or longer (6–8 hours) when possible.

Split red lentils These are specially useful because they cook – unsoaked – in 20 minutes. Use them to make a thick, nourishing soup (page 117), which can make a filling meal if you serve it with wholewheat bread; or make them into a sauce to serve with wholewheat pasta (page 164); or the spicy potato and lentil mixture on page 169 with brown rice or sliced raw tomato and chutney.

Wholewheat flour I find cooks can be divided into those who find pastry-making easy and think of a pie as a quick dish, and those who consider it a real labour. If you come into the first group, it's worth having a bag of self-raising 85 per cent or 100 per cent wholewheat flour in the cupboard for making the quick flans on pages 161 and 163. These can be served just with watercress or a simple green salad for a complete main course.

Nuts and seeds Instant protein, which can be added to dishes of cooked vegetables, salads such as the one on page 180, or cereals, to make them into a main course. Cashew nuts are useful, so are almonds (which are the richest in iron) and walnut halves or pieces (make sure these are fresh and not bitter). Peanuts are cheap, nutritious (being especially rich in B vitamins) and tasty if you buy raw shelled ones and roast them yourself.

To roast peanuts, spread them out on a dry baking sheet and bake for about 15 minutes at 200°C (400°F), gas mark 6. The nuts under the skins should be golden brown. Cool, then store. You can rub off the skins, but I don't bother: it's the roasting which makes all the difference to the flavour. I prefer to buy hazel nuts in their skins, from health shops, and roast them in the same way. Sunflower, sesame and pumpkin seeds are also useful: they're pricy, but you only use them in small quantities and they're good sources of many minerals.

Vegetables Some vegetables require far less preparation than others, and these are the ones to choose when you're short of time: medium-large potatoes, for example, which can just be scrubbed and baked, and medium-sized new potatoes which also only need scrubbing before boiling, thus saving time as well as conserving the valuable nutrients just under the skin. Other easy vegetables are cauliflower and broccoli (both of which are especially nutritious), white button mushrooms, large spring onions, firm tomatoes, red and green peppers and cooked beetroot, if you like it (buy it with the skin still on, from the greengrocer). Onions are a bit of a nuisance to prepare, but necessary for flavour; choose large ones, which are least fiddly to peel, and if you don't need the whole onion, keep part of it in a polythene bag in the fridge to save time another day.

I also like to keep in the freezer some packets of 'casserole vegetables' as the basis of quick stews, and one or two small packets of mixed vegetables for adding to cooked millet and rice, along with toasted flaked almonds, to make a pilaf (see page 162). Canned tomatoes are also indispensable. Vegetables for serving with the main dish also need to be of the labour-saving variety: the ones mentioned above, plus easy-to-use salad ingredients such as large-leaf (therefore easy-to-wash) watercress, clean-looking lettuce and celery, also cucumber, and again, cooked beetroot.

Wholewheat pasta Like the cereals, this can make a quick and healthy basis for a meal. I especially like wholewheat pasta rings, which seem lighter in texture than some of the other varieties. Serve with a quickly made tomato sauce (page 165) and grated cheese (or sunflower seeds or toasted flaked almonds) or with the lentil and red pepper mixture on page 164 or the peanut and tomato sauce on page 173.

The recipes in this section are divided into three groups: cereal dishes, including pastry and pasta; pulse dishes, including tofu; and main vegetable and nut dishes.

CEREAL DISHES

Brown Rice with Tomatoes and Nuts

Very quick and simple to make. Serve with a fresh watercress salad.

SERVES 4

225g (8 oz) long-grain brown rice
½ teaspoon salt
600ml (1 pint) water
25g (1 oz) butter or margarine

450g (1 lb) firm tomatoes, skinned and sliced
125g (4 oz) walnut pieces or roasted peanuts
pepper

Put the rice into a saucepan with the salt and water. Bring to the boil, then cover the pan, turn the heat right down and leave undisturbed for 45 minutes. Then turn the heat off and leave the rice to stand for a further 10–15 minutes. Put back over a gentle heat; add the butter or margarine and fork lightly through the rice; then put in the tomatoes and walnuts, turning the mixture gently with a fork until everything is evenly distributed and the tomatoes heated through. Serve at once.

Variation This is also nice with 300g (10 oz) drained cooked red kidney beans instead of the nuts.

Spiced Brown Rice with Curry Sauce

A pleasantly spicy mixture that's good with mango chutney and a salad made from sliced cucumber mixed with natural yoghurt. Cumin seed is one of the traditional spices for stimulating the milk in breast-feeding mothers, but this dish is too spicy for a baby.

SERVES 4

2 tablespoons oil
1 tablespoon turmeric powder
6 cloves

225g (8 oz) long-grain brown rice
600ml (1 pint) water
1 teaspoon salt

For the sauce
1 onion, peeled and chopped
2 tablespoons oil
1 garlic clove, crushed
2 teaspoons cumin seed
2 teaspoons coriander powder

walnut-sized piece fresh ginger, peeled and grated
1 425-g (15-oz) can tomatoes
salt and pepper

Heat the oil in a medium-sized saucepan. Add the turmeric and cloves and fry for 1–2 minutes. Then put in the rice, and stir for a further 2–3 minutes. Pour in the water and add the salt. Bring to the boil, then put a lid on the pan, turn the heat right down and leave to cook very gently for 45 minutes.

Meanwhile make the sauce. Fry the onion gently in the oil, without browning, for 10 minutes, then add the garlic, cumin and coriander powder. Stir over the heat for 1–2 minutes to cook the spices, then add the ginger and tomatoes. Mix well and add some salt and pepper. Stir gently. Cook over a low heat for 15 minutes; serve with the rice.

Buckwheat with Mushrooms, Onions and Tomatoes

Buckwheat is a natural remedy for varicose veins, high blood pressure and piles – so this is a good dish to try if you suffer from any of these. Apart from this, it tastes good and is quick to make: I like to serve it with sliced carrots in the winter, or courgettes in the summer, both sprinkled with parsley for extra iron and calcium.

SERVES 4

600ml (1 pint) water
1 teaspoon yeast extract
225g (8 oz) buckwheat – buy this from the health shop, already roasted
salt
1 large onion, peeled and chopped

3 tablespoons oil
225g (8 oz) button mushrooms, washed and sliced
225g (8 oz) tomatoes, skinned and chopped
pepper

Put the water and yeast extract into a medium-sized saucepan and bring to the boil. Add the buckwheat and a good pinch of salt. Cover, and leave over a very gentle heat for 10 minutes, when the water should have been absorbed and the buckwheat should be fluffy. Meanwhile, fry the onion in the oil for 7 minutes, then put in the mushrooms and tomatoes and cook, uncovered, for a further 3 minutes. Season with salt and pepper. Serve with the buckwheat.

Bulgur Wheat Pilaf with Red Peppers, Nuts and Raisins

Bulgur is wheat which has been cracked and steamed. It takes 15 minutes to prepare – as opposed to 45 minutes for brown rice – and is therefore especially useful for quick meals. In this dish, the nuts and raisins, and also the cinnamon, give a Middle Eastern flavour. Serve with watercress or lettuce salad, and some yoghurt dressing (page 119) if you've time. You can reduce the cost of this recipe by using roasted peanuts instead of the almonds.

SERVES 4

225g (8 oz) bulgur wheat
600ml (1 pint) boiling water
1 teaspoon salt
1 onion, peeled and chopped
1 small red pepper, deseeded
   and chopped

2 tablespoons oil
1 teaspoon cinnamon
125g (4 oz) raisins
125g (4 oz) flaked almonds

Put the wheat into a large bowl with the water and salt. Cover and leave for 15 minutes. Meanwhile fry the onion and pepper in the oil for 10 minutes, then add the cinnamon and stir for a moment or two. Drain the bulgur wheat and add to the onions and peppers, together with the raisins and almonds. Stir gently over the heat for 5–10 minutes, until wheat is heated through, then check seasoning and serve.

Bulgur Wheat with Peach and Raisin Sauce

I like the sweetness of dried fruit with bulgur wheat and especially like the flavour of the dried peaches in this recipe. Again, for economy, roasted peanuts can be used instead of flaked almonds.

SERVES 4

225g (8 oz) bulgur wheat
600ml (1 pint) boiling water
½ teaspoon salt

125g (4 oz) flaked almonds,
   toasted under a grill

For the sauce

125g (4 oz) dried peaches,
   from health shops
300ml (10 fl oz) boiling water
1 onion, peeled and chopped

2 tablespoons oil
1 garlic clove, crushed
1 teaspoon cinnamon
50g (2 oz) raisins

Put the bulgur wheat into a large saucepan with the boiling water and salt. Cover and leave for 15 minutes. Meanwhile make the sauce. Put the peaches into a bowl, cover with boiling water and leave on one side. Fry the onion in the oil for 10 minutes, then add the garlic and cinnamon. Liquidize the peaches together with their soaking water and add to the onion mixture together with the raisins. Heat gently. Heat the bulgur wheat gently for 10 minutes, then drain off any water and add the almonds. Serve immediately, with the sauce.

Cheese, Tomato and Onion Flan

Time is saved in this recipe by not pre-baking the flan case and by using easily prepared ingredients for the filling. The resulting flan is light and the pastry is tender and melts in your mouth.

SERVES 4 AS A MAIN DISH

200g (8 oz) self-raising 85
   per cent flour
pinch of salt

150g (5 oz) butter or
   polyunsaturated margarine

For the filling

50g (2 oz) grated cheese
6 spring onions, chopped
2 tomatoes, skinned and
   sliced

1 egg
150ml (5 fl oz) milk
salt and pepper

Set the oven to 190°C (375°F), gas mark 5. Put a baking tray into the oven to heat up: standing the flan on this helps the base to cook crisply. Grease a 20-cm (8-in) round flan tin or dish. Sift the flour and salt into a bowl. Add the butter or margarine and rub in with your fingertips until the mixture looks like fine breadcrumbs. Gently press the mixture together to make a dough: you won't need any water. Put dough on to a lightly floured board and knead into a smooth circle. Then roll out thinly and lift gently into flan tin or dish. Press down, trim edges. Do not prick. Sprinkle cheese and spring onions over pastry, then arrange tomatoes on top and sprinkle with salt and pepper. Whisk egg and milk in a bowl with a little seasoning, then pour over tomatoes. Put the flan into the oven and bake for 40 minutes, until pastry is crisp and golden brown and centre is set and puffed up. Serve immediately, with a lettuce and cucumber salad or frozen peas and new potatoes.

If you don't eat dairy produce Make filling as for the mushroom and tofu flan (page 163), using 125g (4 oz) skinned, chopped tomatoes instead of the mushrooms.

Millet Pilaf with Mixed Vegetables

Millet, which you can buy at health food shops, cooks in 20 minutes and has an attractive pale golden colour and a pleasant flavour which makes a change from rice.

SERVES 4

1 onion, peeled and chopped
2 tablespoons oil
225g (8 oz) millet
600ml (1 pint) water
½ teaspoon salt

1 125-g (4-oz) packet frozen
  mixed vegetables
125g (4 oz) roasted peanuts, see
  page 154

Fry the onion in the oil in a medium-sized saucepan for 10 minutes. Then add the millet, water, salt and mixed vegetables and bring to the boil. Cover, turn the heat down and leave to cook for 20 minutes, when millet should be fluffy and water absorbed. Add the peanuts, fork through lightly, then serve. It's nice with some sliced tomatoes and watercress.

Millet with Almonds (or Peanuts) and Tomato Sauce

SERVES 4

1 onion, peeled and chopped
2 tablespoons oil
225g (8 oz) millet
600ml (1 pint) water
1 teaspoon salt

125g (4 oz) flaked almonds,
  toasted under the grill – or,
  for economy, use peanuts,
  roasted as on page 154

For the sauce
1 onion, peeled and chopped
2 tablespoons oil

1 425-g (15-oz) can tomatoes

Fry the onion in the oil in a medium-sized saucepan for 10 minutes:

Then add the millet, water and salt and bring to the boil. Cover, turn the heat down and leave to cook for 20 minutes, when millet should be fluffy and water absorbed. Meanwhile, make the sauce. Fry the onion in the oil for 10 minutes, until soft, then add the tomatoes. Liquidize. Season and return to the pan. Add the flaked almonds or peanuts to the millet, fork through lightly, then serve with the tomato sauce. Some watercress or lettuce in a light oil and vinegar dressing (page 125) goes well with this.

Mushroom Flan with Tofu

The custard part of this is made from tofu (soya bean curd, see page 153), yet it is almost identical to a light custard made from eggs and cream.

SERVES 4 AS A MAIN DISH

100g (4 oz) self-raising 85 per cent flour
pinch of salt

65g (2½ oz) polyunsaturated margarine

For the filling

1 onion, peeled and finely chopped
25g (1 oz) vegetable margarine
1 garlic clove, crushed, optional
125g (4 oz) white button mushrooms, washed and thinly sliced

1 300-g (10½-oz) packet tofu
salt and pepper
25g (1 oz) ground almonds

Set the oven to 190°C (375°F), gas mark 5. Put a baking tray into the oven to heat up: standing the flan on this helps the base to cook crisply. Grease a 20-cm (8-in) round flan tin or dish. Sift the flour and salt into a bowl. Rub in the margarine with your fingertips until the mixture looks like fine breadcrumbs. Gently press together to make a dough: you won't need any water. Put dough on to a lightly floured board and knead into a smooth circle. Then roll out thinly and lift gently into flan dish or tin. Press down, trim edges. Do not prick.

Fry the onion gently in the margarine for 7 minutes, then put in the garlic and mushrooms and cook for a further 3 minutes. Remove from the heat, then stir in the tofu. Season with salt and pepper. Spoon into flan case, level top, sprinkle with the ground almonds. Put the flan into the oven and bake for 40 minutes, until pastry is crisp and golden brown and centre is set and puffed up. Serve immediately; it's good with new potatoes and a salad of watercress and lettuce, or frozen peas.

Pasta with Lentil and Red Pepper Sauce

A quickly made, iron-rich dish. I like it best with wholewheat pasta rings, rather than spaghetti. When funds allow, some cheapish red wine, such as a Bulgarian Cabernet Sauvignon, goes very well with this: add a couple of tablespoons to the sauce before serving, too.

SERVES 4

1 onion, peeled and chopped	400ml (¾ pint) water
1 small red pepper, deseeded and chopped	salt and pepper
	sugar
2 tablespoons oil	225g (8 oz) wholewheat
1 garlic clove, crushed	spaghetti or rings
1 teaspoon dried basil	15g (½ oz) butter
1 225-g (8-oz) can tomatoes	grated cheese to serve,
125g (4 oz) split red lentils	optional
1 tablespoon tomato purée	

Fry the onion and pepper in the oil in a large saucepan for 10 minutes, then put in the garlic, basil, tomatoes, lentils, purée and salted water. Bring to the boil, then turn the heat down and leave to simmer gently, uncovered, for 15–20 minutes, until the lentils are cooked. Season with salt, pepper and a dash of sugar. About 15 minutes before the sauce is ready, start cooking the pasta. Half-fill a large saucepan with lightly salted water and bring to the boil. Add the pasta, easing spaghetti down into the water as the ends soften. Boil rapidly, uncovered, for about 10 minutes, until a piece feels just tender when you bite it. Drain, then return to the pan with the butter and salt and pepper to taste. Serve with the sauce, and hand round grated cheese, if you're having this. Some watercress or green salad is nice with it, too.

Wholewheat Pasta Rings with Tomato Sauce

A beautifully quick dish; serve with watercress or a watercress-based salad.

SERVES 4

1 onion, peeled and chopped
2 tablespoons oil
1 425-g (15-oz) can tomatoes
salt and pepper
350g (12 oz) wholewheat pasta
  rings

15g (½ oz) butter
grated cheese or vegan cheese
  (page 133) to serve

Fry the onion in the oil in a medium-sized saucepan for 10 minutes, until softened, then add the tomatoes, liquidize, return to pan, season, keep warm. Meanwhile cook the pasta in a large saucepan half-filled with boiling, salted water: it will take 8–10 minutes. Drain it when it is just tender, then return the pasta to the pan with the butter and seasoning. Serve the pasta rings with the sauce and hand round grated cheese.

Quick Pizza

Wholewheat pitta bread makes an excellent base for a quick pizza.
Serve with watercress or lettuce salad.

SERVES 4

4 wholewheat pitta breads	125–175g (4–6 oz) grated
225g (8 oz) cottage cheese	cheese
8 tomatoes, skinned and	salt and pepper
sliced	oregano

Set oven to 200°C (400°F), gas mark 6, or prepare a hot grill. Put
the pitta bread on a baking sheet. Spread each with cottage cheese,
arrange the tomato slices on top and scatter grated cheese over
them. Sprinkle with salt, pepper and oregano. Bake in the oven
for about 20 minutes, or place under grill for about 10 minutes,
until filling has heated through and cheese has melted and
browned.

If you don't eat dairy produce Use a 300-g (10½-oz) packet tofu,
drained, mashed and seasoned, or butter bean spread (page 130)
instead of cottage cheese, and vegan cheese (page 133) for the
topping.

BEAN AND LENTIL DISHES

Quick Curried Butter Beans

More warming spices for breast-feeding mums. Serve with hot,
boiled brown rice. (This is too spicy for a baby.)

SERVES 4

1 onion, peeled and chopped
2 tablespoons oil
1 garlic clove, crushed
2 teaspoons cumin seed
2 teaspoons coriander powder
walnut-sized piece fresh ginger, peeled

600g (1 lb 4 oz) cooked butter beans (page 135) – or 2 425-g (15-oz) cans
150ml (5 fl oz) water, or cooking water drained from the butter beans, if available
salt and pepper

Fry the onion gently in the oil, without browning, for 10 minutes, then the garlic, cumin and coriander powder. Stir over the heat for 1–2 minutes to cook the spices, then add the ginger, butter beans and water. Mix well and add some salt and pepper. Cook over a low heat for 15 minutes.

Creamed Chickpeas with Croutons

Very easy and delicious. Serve with some sliced tomatoes.

SERVES 4

1 onion, peeled and chopped
2 tablespoons oil, preferably olive
1 garlic clove, crushed
600g (1 lb 4 oz) cooked chickpeas (page 135) – or 2 425-g (15-oz) cans

150ml (5 fl oz) water, or cooking water drained from the chickpeas, if available
1–2 tablespoons lemon juice
salt and pepper

For the croutons
3–4 pieces wholewheat bread

oil for shallow-frying

Fry the onion gently in the oil, without browning, for 10 minutes, then the garlic and chickpeas. Mash the chickpeas. Add the water, beating with a wooden spoon to make a light mixture, like mashed potatoes. Add the lemon juice and salt and pepper to taste. Keep mixture warm while you make the croutons. Cut the crusts off the bread, then cut the bread into small dice. Fry in hot shallow fat until golden brown, turning them so that they brown all over. Drain on kitchen paper. Serve the chickpea cream with the croutons.

Variation The chickpea cream can be served with hot fingers of wholewheat toast if preferred.

Chilli Red Beans

Another quick and easy bean dish that's good with some hot brown rice and a quickly made green salad. If you're making this for a baby to share, remove the baby's portion before adding the chilli powder and seasoning.

SERVES 4

1 onion, peeled and chopped
1 red pepper, deseeded and
  chopped
2 tablespoons oil
1 425-g (15-oz) can tomatoes
1 425-g (15-oz) can red kidney
  beans – or home-cooked
  beans (see page 135),
  drained

1 teaspoon chilli powder
salt and pepper
hot, cooked brown rice to
  serve

Fry the onion and red pepper gently in the oil, without browning, for 10 minutes, then add tomatoes, red kidney beans, chilli powder and salt and pepper to taste. Stir over a gentle heat for 5–10 minutes, until beans are heated through. Serve with hot, cooked brown rice or mashed potatoes.

Easy Cheesy Lentils

This is cheap and nourishing, and rich in iron and calcium. Serve with sliced tomatoes and watercress.

SERVES 4

1 onion, peeled and chopped	750ml (1¼ pint) water
2 tablespoons oil	125g (4 oz) grated cheese
1 garlic clove, crushed	salt and pepper
225g (8 oz) split red lentils	

Fry the onion in the oil in a large saucepan for 10 minutes. Add the garlic, lentils and water. Bring to the boil, then cover, turn down the heat and cook gently for 15–20 minutes, until lentils are pale and soft. Beat in the grated cheese and season with salt and pepper. Serve at once.

If you don't eat diary produce Use vegan cheese (page 133) instead of dairy cheese; season lentils carefully – you may need to add a little yeast extract or miso and lemon juice.

Spicy Lentils and Potatoes

This is quick, easy and cheap; it's a good source of iron, which is found in both lentils and potatoes, and contains the warming spices which are helpful for breast-feeding. Serve with slices of firm raw tomato and some mango chutney. If a baby is going to share this with you, keep one section of the pan free from spices and avoid stirring this area. Serve the baby this portion first, then stir gently before serving out the rest.

SERVES 4

1 onion, peeled and chopped
2 tablespoons oil
1 garlic clove, crushed
1 teaspoon whole cumin seeds
walnut-sized piece of fresh
  ginger, peeled and finely
  grated

3 medium-sized potatoes,
  peeled and cut into 2-cm (1-
  in) cubes
225g (8 oz) split red lentils
750ml (1¼ pint) water
salt and pepper

Fry the onion in the oil for 10 minutes in a large saucepan or large, deep, frying pan. Add the garlic, cumin and ginger; stir-fry for 1–2 minutes, then put in the potatoes and stir for a further minute or two. Add the lentils, water and a little seasoning, bring to the boil, then cover, turn down the heat and cook gently for 15–20 minutes, until lentils are pale and soft and potatoes just tender when pierced with a knife. Check seasoning, serve at once.

Tofu Fritters with Lemon

Meat-eaters compare this to fried fish. Delicious with the yoghurt dressing on page 119, or parsley sauce, page 138, and a salad or quickly cooked vegetable. You need to allow time for the tofu to drain.

SERVES 4

2 300-g (10-oz) packets tofu –
  from health shops
salt and pepper
lemon juice

wholewheat flour
oil for shallow-frying
lemon wedges

Drain the tofu carefully, being careful not to break it up. Then wrap each block of tofu in a clean absorbent cloth, place in a colander and arrange a weight on top. Leave for several hours – overnight and during the following day if possible – to drain and firm up. Then cut into slices, sprinkle each with salt, pepper and a few drops of lemon juice and coat in flour. Shallow-fry until crisp and golden brown on both sides. Drain on kitchen paper. Serve at once, with the lemon wedges.

MAIN COURSE VEGETABLE AND NUT DISHES

Several of these vegetable dishes are good with a crunchy savoury seed mix sprinkled over them.

To make this savoury seed mix, mix 2 heaped tablespoons sesame seeds and 2 heaped tablespoons pumpkin seeds, sunflower seeds or roasted peanuts with 2 tablespoons Shoyu soy sauce. Make sure that all the seeds or nuts are coated with soy sauce. Spread the mixture out on a dry baking sheet and bake at 200°C (400°F), gas mark 6, for 10–15 minutes. Cool on tray: the mixture will get crisp as it cools. You can of course make this in a larger quantity if you like it. I find it very useful, and it's especially good with some pine kernels added – if ever you're feeling rich and extravagant.

Quick Almond and Mushroom Nutmeat

Serve this with new potatoes and a cooked green vegetable; or use it as a filling for parboiled green peppers, then bake. It's also good as a filling for a baked, wholewheat, flan case. This dish contains iron – in the almonds, bread and parsley.

SERVES 4

150ml (5 fl oz) boiling water
1 teaspoon yeast extract
4 slices wholewheat bread, crusts removed
1 onion, peeled and finely chopped
2 tablespoons oil
125g (4 oz) button mushrooms, washed and sliced

125g (4 oz) almonds, finely grated
1 tablespoon Shoyu soy sauce
1 tablespoon lemon juice
salt and pepper
chopped parsley and lemon wedges, to serve

Put the boiling water, yeast extract and bread into a bowl. Leave on one side. Fry the onion in the oil, for 7 minutes, browning slightly, then add the mushrooms and fry for 3 minutes more. Stir in the bread and water mixture, the almonds, soy sauce, lemon juice and seasoning. Mix gently, cook for a few minutes longer to heat everything through, then serve, sprinkled with chopped parsley and garnished with lemon wedges. Some fingers of hot wholewheat toast are pleasant with this, if you want a crisp texture to contrast.

Easy Cauliflower Cheese

SERVES 4

1 large cauliflower   225g (8 oz) grated cheese
salt

Preheat a moderately hot grill. Wash and trim the cauliflower, dividing it into small florets as you do so. Heat 2cm (1 in) salted water in a saucepan, put in the cauliflower and cook for about 4 minutes, until just tender. Drain well and place in a lightly greased, shallow, ovenproof dish. Cover with the grated cheese and place under the grill until the cheese has melted and is beginning to brown. Serve immediately, with hot wholewheat toast or rolls, and a salad of watercress or sliced tomatoes.

If you don't eat dairy produce Use vegan cheese (page 133) instead of dairy cheese.

Cauliflower with Peanut and Tomato Sauce

This is suitable for a baby to share as long as you grind up the peanuts finely.

SERVES 4

1 large cauliflower   salt

For the sauce
1 onion, peeled and chopped   450g (1 lb) tomatoes, skinned
2 tablespoons oil   and chopped
1 tablespoon peanut butter   pepper
125g (4 oz) roasted peanuts (see
   page 154), chopped or
   grated

Start by making the sauce. Fry the onion in the oil for 10 minutes, then add the peanut butter, peanuts and tomatoes. Season with pepper and keep warm. Wash and trim the cauliflower, dividing it into small florets as you do so. Heat 2cm (1 in) salted water in a saucepan, put in the cauliflower and cook for about 5 minutes, until tender. Serve cauliflower with the sauce spooned over it.

Quick Nut Rissoles

Another recipe containing buckwheat, with its valuable rutin, and iron from the almonds and parsley.

SERVES 4

1 onion, peeled and finely chopped
50g (2 oz) polyunsaturated margarine
50g (2 oz) buckwheat flour – from health shops
300ml (10 fl oz) water
1 teaspoon yeast extract

225g (8 oz) almonds, finely grated
1 teaspoon mixed herbs
2 heaped tablespoons chopped parsley, if available
salt and pepper
wholewheat flour, to coat
oil for shallow-frying

Fry the onion in the margarine for 10 minutes. Stir in the buckwheat flour, then the water, to make a thick sauce. Cook for 3–4 minutes, then remove from the heat and add the rest of the ingredients except the coating, and season to taste. If there's time, cool mixture; in any case, form into rissoles, coat in flour, oatmeal or crumbs and shallow-fry, turning rissoles to cook both sides. Serve with a green salad, or with chutney in a soft, wholewheat bap, or with vegetarian gravy (page 137) and cooked vegetables – carrots and mashed potatoes go particularly well with these.

Baked Potatoes with Various Toppings

One of the great convenience foods, a jacket-baked potato makes
an excellent simple main course. Grated cheese is probably the
most popular topping – but cottage cheese or soured cream or
yoghurt and chopped chives are also good.

If you don't eat dairy produce Tofu mashed with chopped chives or
spring onions, grated hard soya cheese, or one of the bean or nut
spreads on pages 130–4 are also good for a change. One of my
daughters likes her jacket potato best with the homemade tomato
sauce on page 139.

SERVES 4

4 medium-large potatoes,   topping as required: see above
   about 225g (8 oz) each
oil

Preheat oven to 230°C (450°F), gas mark 8. Scrub potatoes, then
prick in several places to allow steam to escape. Rub potatoes
lightly with oil if liked, then place them in a baking tin and bake
for 1–1½ hours, until the potatoes feel soft when squeezed lightly
in the centre. Serve with the selected topping, or with one of the
salads in this section: they're particularly good with the cabbage
salad on page 123.

Potato Cakes with Nuts or Sunflower Seeds

These are especially quick if you plan them in advance and cook
extra potatoes the previous day. They're nice with the cabbage
salad on pages 123-4, or with a simple salad of lettuce and sliced
tomatoes.

SERVES 4

450g (1 lb) potatoes
15g (½ oz) butter or
    margarine
milk or soya milk
125g (4 oz) almonds, cashew
    nuts or sunflower seeds,
    finely ground

2 tablespoons chopped spring
    onion
salt and pepper
wholewheat flour for coating
oil for shallow-frying

Scrub or peel the potatoes, cut into even-sized pieces. Cover with
water and boil gently until tender, then drain and mash. (You can
mash them with the skins on for extra fibre and nourishment if you
like.) Beat in the butter or margarine and the milk to make a
creamy consistency, then add the nuts or sunflower seeds and
spring onion. Stir in a little more milk if necessary to make a soft
consistency which holds together. Season with salt and pepper.
Divide into 8 pieces, form into 'cakes' and coat in wholewheat
flour. Fry quickly in a little hot, shallow fat; drain on kitchen
paper. Serve at once.

Main Course Mashed Potatoes

One of my emergency stand-bys when I was hard-pressed with two babies under two years old. I would serve this with watercress or frozen peas.

SERVES 4

1kg (2 lb 4 oz) potatoes, peeled and cut into even-sized pieces
15g (½ oz) butter or margarine
200ml (6 fl oz) milk or soya milk
175g (6 oz) grated cheese
salt and pepper
2 tomatoes, sliced

Boil the potatoes until tender, drain and mash with the butter and milk. Prepare a hot grill. Beat in most of the grated cheese, season with salt and pepper. Spread mixture in grill pan or suitable ovenproof dish. Put tomato slices on top, sprinkle with rest of cheese. Grill until top is golden brown. Serve at once.

If you don't eat dairy produce You could use vegan cheese, page 133, instead of dairy cheese, but a better variation, I think, is to mix a heaped tablespoon each of sesame seeds and sunflower seeds with a tablespoon of Shoyu soy sauce and sprinkle this all over the top before grilling. Don't have the dish too near the grill flame: sesame seeds catch easily.

Easy Ratatouille

Ratatouille is economical if you make it when courgettes are in season, and it can be served as a main dish, with cooked rice, millet, bulgur wheat or buckwheat, or potatoes to accompany it. This is suitable for a baby if you mash her portion.

SERVES 4

2 large onions, peeled and chopped
2 tablespoons oil
1 large garlic clove, crushed
2 red peppers, deseeded and chopped

450g (1 lb) courgettes, washed and sliced
1 425-g (15-oz) can tomatoes
salt and pepper
chopped parsley to serve, optional

Fry the onions gently in the oil in a large saucepan for 10 minutes without browning. Add the garlic, red peppers and courgettes and fry for a further 5 minutes, stirring often. Then stir in the tomatoes and some salt and pepper. Cook gently for 15 minutes, until vegetables are tender. Check seasoning, and serve sprinkled with lots of chopped parsley, if available. Alternatively, fork plenty of chopped parsley into the brown rice or other grains to give them a pretty green colour and add to the nourishment of the dish.

Stir-Fried Vegetables

These are quick to do as long as you choose vegetables which do not need much preparation. I like to use broccoli because it is such an attractive colour, and one of the most nutritious vegetables of all. Use home-grown bean sprouts (page 121) if you have them.

SERVES 4

2 tablespoons oil
750g (1½ lb) broccoli,
  washed, trimmed and cut
  into small pieces
1 small red pepper, deseeded
  and finely chopped
350g (12 oz) bean sprouts,
  washed

bunch of spring onions,
  trimmed and chopped
walnut-sized piece of fresh
  ginger, finely grated
salt and pepper
125g (4 oz) almonds, roasted
  peanuts or pumpkin seeds

Just before you want to eat, heat the oil in a wok or large saucepan. Put in all the vegetables and the ginger and stir-fry for 1–2 minutes, until they're heated through. Season; stir in the nuts or seeds. Serve with hot brown rice, millet, bulgur wheat or warm pitta bread – if you're serving it with cereals, remember to get these cooked before you start stir-frying!

Vegetable Stew

Although aubergine isn't usually the cheapest of vegetables, this stew can make quite an economical main course if you serve it with some cooked grains: millet or bulgur wheat go well with it, and some cooked pulses can be added, too.

SERVES 4

1 large aubergine	pepper
salt	2 sticks celery, sliced
1 large onion, peeled and chopped	350g (12 oz) carrots, scraped and sliced
3 tablespoons oil	50g (2 oz) button mushrooms, washed and sliced
2 garlic cloves, crushed	chopped parsley
1 425-g (15-oz) can tomatoes	

Trim stalk from aubergine. Cut aubergine into 1-cm (½-in) dice, put into a colander, sprinkle with salt and leave under a weight for about 30 minutes. Then rinse under cold water and squeeze as dry as possible in your hand. Fry the onion in 1 tablespoon of the oil for 10 minutes. Add the garlic and tomatoes, liquidize and season. Heat the rest of the oil in a large saucepan and fry the aubergine, celery, carrots and mushrooms for 10 minutes. Add the tomato mixture. Cook over a gentle heat until the vegetables are tender. Serve with hot, cooked, brown rice and hand round the protein topping on page 171 separately, if liked.

Puddings

From the health point of view, fresh fruit really is the best pudding there is, so there's no need to feel you have to serve a pudding for nourishment. If you think that fresh fruit is expensive, it's worth checking the price of fruit in season with that of a 'proper' pudding: it usually compares favourably. However, I know many families don't feel they've had a meal unless they finish with a pudding, so here are some ideas for puddings which are quick and nutritious.

First of all, three useful toppings which taste good and are much better for you than cream, and a crunchy garnish which is a good way of adding some nutritious sesame seeds to a pudding.

Creamy Tofu and Almond Topping

This works out cheaper than a large 300-ml (10-fl oz) carton of whipping cream, but unlike cream, contains useful amounts of iron, calcium and other minerals.

SERVES 4

150g (5 oz) tofu
25g (1 oz) ground almonds
1 teaspoon honey
½–1 teaspoon vanilla essence – real vanilla essence from health shops, if possible

Drain excess water off tofu, then put the tofu into a bowl with the other ingredients and beat until creamy.

Whipped Tofu Topping

This one also works out cheaper than a large carton of double cream. it has a lovely whipped texture, like double cream, but, like the tofu and almond topping, is nutritious.

SERVES 4

150g (5 oz) tofu – from health shops, see page 153
50g (2 oz) unsalted polyunsaturated margarine, such as Vitaquell, from health shops
25g (1 oz) light barbados sugar, from health shops
½–1 teaspoon vanilla essence – real vanilla essence from health shops, if possible

Drain the tofu in a sieve, then blot it dry with a soft cloth. Beat the margarine and sugar until light and fluffy, then gradually add the tofu, a little at a time, beating well between each addition, to make a light, fluffy mixture. Flavour with vanilla.

Cashew Nut or Almond Cream

A pleasant, pouring cream which is delicious over fruit salads, and dried fruit compotes like the one on page 187. It works out at about the same price as a large carton of whipping cream. You need a liquidizer to make it.

MAKES 300ML (10 FL OZ)

125g (4 oz) cashew nuts – broken ones are fine
150ml (5 fl oz) water
1–2 teaspoons light barbados sugar or honey

Put all the ingredients into the liquidizer goblet and whizz to a cream. Can be thinned with a little more water, if you like.

Crunchy Sesame Topping

This is marvellous sprinkled over natural yoghurt, or over a creamy pudding like the apricot fool on page 185, and it keeps well in an airtight jar. Sesame seeds are rich in calcium.

1 teaspoon butter or margarine
50g (2 oz) demerara sugar – make sure it's the real thing, from health shops
25g (1 oz) sesame seeds

Put the butter or margarine and sugar into a small saucepan and heat gently, until the sugar has melted, lost its granular appearance and is bubbling at the edges. This only takes a couple of minutes or so. Then remove from the heat, stir in the sesame seeds and turn the mixture out on to a piece of non-stick paper. Spread it out with a knife or the palm of your hand so that it is about 6mm (¼ in) thick. Cool, then crush into little chunky pieces with a rolling pin.

Healthy Baked Apples

Easy, nutritious and delicious served with the tofu and almond topping, page 181, the cashew nut or almond cream, page 182, or some chilled natural yoghurt.

SERVES 4

4 medium-sized cooking apples
125g (4 oz) raisins

Set oven to 200°C (400°F), gas mark 6. Wash apples and remove core, then score round the centre of each with a sharp knife. Place apples in ovenproof dish. Fill centres with raisins. Bake for 45 minutes, until apples are tender.

Apple and Raisin Compote

In this recipe, the raisins add extra food value (iron and B vitamins) as well as sweetness, so that little or no extra sweetening is needed. If this is sieved or liquidized after cooking, it's excellent for a baby.

SERVES 4

900g (2 lb) apples
2 tablespoons water or orange juice
225g (8 oz) raisins
clear honey to taste

Peel, core and slice the apples. Heat the water or orange juice in a heavy-based saucepan and put in the apples and raisins. Stir, then cover and leave to cook gently for about 10 minutes, until the apples are soft. Stir mixture from time to time as it cooks, to avoid burning. This is good either hot or cold.

To freeze Cool quickly, spoon into suitable container, freeze. To use, allow to thaw for several hours at room temperature.

Apricots with Cashew Nut Cream

This is a particularly nutritious pudding, being especially rich in vitamin A, calcium and iron, and a pleasant mixture of flavours and textures. It's best to soak the apricots overnight if possible. Liquidize the apricots if serving to a baby.

SERVES 4

450g (1 lb) dried apricots
125g (4 oz) cashew nuts
1–2 teaspoons honey
½ teaspoon vanilla essence

Wash the apricots well in warm water, then put them into a bowl and leave to soak for several hours. If they seem soft enough to eat as they are, just drain off (and keep) most of the water and put the apricots in serving dishes. If they seem rather firm, put them into a saucepan with their soaking water and simmer gently, without a lid, until the apricots are tender and the water has become syrupy. Cool, then put into serving dishes as before. To make the topping, put the cashew nuts into a blender or food processor with the honey, vanilla and 150ml (5 fl oz) water – if you drained the apricots, use this water. Blend until creamy-looking and fairly smooth, adding a little more water if necessary to make the consistency you want. Pour over the apricots to serve.

To freeze The prepared apricots and the topping can be frozen separately in suitable containers. To use, remove from freezer and leave to stand at room temperature for 2–3 hours, or until thawed. Stir topping before use.

Apricot Fool

This is not a cheap pudding, but it is easy to make and rich in both iron and calcium. An excellent pudding for a baby.

SERVES 4

450g (1 lb) dried apricots
350g (12 oz) soft, white, low-fat cheese such as quark or fromage
    blanc, or a 300-g (10½-oz) packet tofu, firmed up as described
    on page 153
2 tablespoons honey
sesame crunch (page 183) to garnish, optional

Wash the apricots well in warm water, then soak in cold water for several hours. If they still seem rather firm after this, cook them gently in their soaking liquid until tender, then cool. Drain the apricots, then put them into a blender or food processor with the white, low-fat cheese, or the tofu and the honey, and blend until smooth. Spoon into individual bowls, sprinkle with the sesame crunch just before serving, if liked.

To freeze Spoon mixture into a suitable container, freeze. To use, thaw at room temperature for several hours.

Easy Uncooked Non-Dairy Cheesecake

A creamy, special-occasion pudding – rather too rich for a baby.

MAKES ONE 20-CM (8-IN) CHEESECAKE SERVING 4

1 300-g (10½-oz) packet tofu
125g (4 oz) unsalted polyunsaturated margarine, such as Vitaquell, from health shops
50g (2 oz) light barbados sugar, from health shops
1 teaspoon vanilla essence – real vanilla, from health shops, if possible
125g (4 oz) crunchy granola-type breakfast cereal
a little crunchy sesame topping to garnish, optional

Drain the tofu, then wrap it in a clean, absorbent cloth, place in a colander, put a weight on top and leave for at least 1 hour to firm up. Cream the margarine and sugar. Add the tofu, a little at a time, beating well after each addition, then beat in the vanilla. Put the crunchy breakfast cereal in the base of a 20-cm (8-in) flan dish. Spoon the tofu mixture on top, level the surface. Chill for 2–3 hours. Sprinkle with the sesame crunch just before serving, if liked.

Dried Fruit Compote

This is packed with iron and other minerals. It's good on its own or with natural yoghurt or the cashew nut or almond cream on page 182. Liquidize or sieve if serving to a baby.

SERVES 4

450g (1 lb) dried fruit salad mix, from health shops
boiling water

Wash the dried fruit well in warm water, then put it into a bowl, cover generously with boiling water and leave to soak for several hours. After that, put the fruit into a saucepan, together with the water in which it was soaked, and simmer gently, without a lid, until the fruit is tender and the water syrupy and much reduced. Cool, then chill.

To freeze Spoon the fruit into a suitable container, leaving room for expansion, freeze. To use, remove from freezer and leave to stand at room temperature for several hours, or until thawed.

Figs with Yoghurt and Sesame Seeds

This pudding supplies over half the recommended daily calcium allowance during pregnancy, so if, like me, you're fond of these particular ingredients, it's a useful pudding (or breakfast) dish.

SERVES 1

125g (4 oz) dried figs, chopped
150ml (5 fl oz) natural yoghurt
1 rounded tablespoon sesame seeds

Put the the figs into a bowl, pour the yoghurt over and sprinkle with the sesame seeds

Fruit Salad

Any fruit in season can be used for this, and because of their high nutritional value, I often slip in a few dried fruits, too, as in this recipe.

SERVES 4

125g (4 oz) dried whole apricots, from health shops
8–10 small prunes
boiling water
2 large juicy oranges
1 large eating apple, with a rosy skin if possible, washed
1 banana

Put the dried apricots and prunes into a bowl and cover with boiling water. Leave to soak for several hours, then stew them gently in a saucepan, with their soaking water, for about 20 minutes if necessary, to make them more tender. Cool and put into a bowl. Hold the oranges over the bowl (to catch the juice) and cut off the skin, going round and round like peeling an apple. Then cut the segments of flesh away from the skin and membranes. Slice the apple, peel and slice the banana, and add to the bowl. Spoon into individual serving dishes. This is good on its own, or with one of the toppings on page 182.

Muesli, Original Version

Although most people think of muesli as a breakfast dish, it was originally a fruit dish, invented by Dr Bircher Benner at the turn of the century to try to get the patients at this health clinic in Zurich to eat more fresh fruit. The composition of his original dish was said to be very close to breast milk. It makes a good dish for toddlers, either as a pudding or main dish, and is another one that's useful if you're fancying small, frequent meals when you're pregnant or breast-feeding. This is Dr Bircher Benner's original recipe.

SERVES 1

1 tablespoon sweetened condensed milk
1 tablespoon lemon juice
1 tablespoon rolled oats
1 large eating apple
1 tablespoon chopped or grated hazel nuts or almonds – finely ground if you're giving this to a toddler

Put the condensed milk and lemon juice into a bowl and mix together, then add the oats. Wash the apple, then grate fairly coarsely into the bowl. If the mixture is too stiff, add a little water. Spoon into a bowl and sprinkle with the nuts. If you're serving this as a pudding, it's nice with some single cream.

If you don't eat dairy produce Leave out the condensed milk and make the mixture with soya milk or vegan yoghurt (page 191), and add clear honey to taste.

Muesli, Oaty Version

As I've explained above, muesli needn't be just a cereal dish eaten at breakfast. I often make a fruity version and serve it as a pudding. This dish contains oats to help counteract depression, apples and orange juice for vitamin C, yoghurt for calcium and almonds and raisins for iron. Babies love this; grate the apples finely and powder the oats and almonds in a blender if you're making it for a baby.

SERVES 4

3 large apples, washed and grated, skin, core and all
150 ml (5 fl oz) orange juice
125g (4 oz) rolled oats, or a mixture of oats and barley flakes from
   the health shop
1 tablespoon clear honey
50g (2 oz) raisins
50g (2 oz) flaked almonds – or use roasted peanuts (see page 154)
   for economy

Put all the ingredients except the almonds (or peanuts) into a bowl
and mix together. Spoon into bowls, sprinkle with the nuts. This
is lovely, if you want to spoil yourself, with some single cream on
top.

If you don't eat dairy produce Use vegan yoghurt (page 191).

Yoghurt, Banana and Crunchy Granola

A quick pudding or nutritious breakfast dish or snack.

SERVES 1

1 banana
2 tablespoons natural yoghurt
1–2 tablespoons crunchy breakfast cereal
clear honey

Slice the banana and put into a serving bowl. Pour the yoghurt over
the honey and sprinkle with the crunchy cereal. Spoon a little clear
honey over the top, if liked.

If you don't eat dairy produce Use vegan yoghurt (page 191).

Vegan Yoghurt

MAKES 450ML (1 PINT)

450ml (1 pint) soya milk
yoghurt starter culture, from health shops

Any yoghurt culture will work as well on soya milk as it does on
dairy milk. Put the soya milk into a saucepan and bring to the boil,
then cool to lukewarm. Add the starter as directed on the packet,
stir well. Pour the mixture into a large jar or bowl, which has been
sterilized by being rinsed out with boiling water. Cover the jar with
clingfilm or foil, leave in a warm place for 6–8 hours until set, then
chill in the fridge. This first batch will not be 100 per cent vegan,
but you can use a tablespoonful of it for the next batch (and so on
for subsequent ones) and they will be. The yoghurt gets thicker
and better and sweeter each time.

Cakes, Biscuits and Sweets

When cakes, biscuits and sweets are made with wholesome ingredients such as wholewheat flour, nuts, dried fruit, molasses, and not too much fat and sugar, they can be nutritious – rich in iron and B vitamins – as well as delicious. And strange though it may seem, they can be just what you fancy, particularly in the early days of pregnancy if you're prone to sudden hunger-pangs and/or nausea, and when you're breast-feeding, especially in the early days when your milk supply is becoming established. So don't feel guilty if you fancy something sweet, but make sure what you have is as nourishing and wholesome as possible, as in the recipes which follow. Homemade cakes and biscuits are also useful for taking to the hospital, for your partner (see pages 48–9) during your labour, and for you immediately after the birth if you feel, as many of us do, that you need some quick energy.

All the cakes in this section freeze well, so it might be worth making up some extra batches of your favourites to cheer you up in those hectic days after the baby is born. The fruit cakes and slices, and the parkin, keep well in a tin for two weeks, as do the crunchy bars.

Note on ingredients

Flour All the recipes are at their healthiest when made with 100 per cent wholewheat (or wholemeal, the two terms are interchangeable) flour, though if you're not used to this you might prefer at first to mix this half and half with your normal flour, or use an 81–85 per cent flour which you can get at health shops and which is lighter than a 100 per cent flour, while retaining some of the goodness. If you have any problems with constipation either during pregnancy or after the birth, though, you'd find the extra bran in wholewheat flour helpful. I prefer to buy plain 100 per cent wholewheat flour, which is easy to obtain, and add baking powder.

Fat I use vegetable oil or a soft margarine that is high in polyunsaturates (may also be described as low-cholesterol but should still state high in polyunsaturates on the tub). This is more expensive than ordinary soft margarine, but it's an expense which I consider worthwhile from the health point of view. If you're using oil, make sure that this, too, is polyunsaturated: sunflower, corn and soya oils are; 'vegetable oil' probably isn't.

Sugar and sweeteners Until recently I had thought that all sugar – brown, white or in between – is basically a bad thing, and like many people I've been trying to reduce the amount of sugar I use. While writing this book and looking at sources of iron, I was therefore quite surprised to see how much iron real dark brown barbados molasses sugar contains (over twice as much, weight for weight, as, for instance, dried prunes, which are considered to be a good source). And of course molasses and black treacle (which are very similar) have always been known as an excellent source of iron and also calcium.

So, while I still think that white sugar should be used with great caution and avoided as far as possible, I have somewhat revised my opinion where real brown sugar is concerned. It is important, however, to make sure you get (and still use in moderation only) real barbados molasses sugar, which you can buy at health shops: it's the ordinary brown sugars which are virtually the same nutritionally as white sugar.

Bran, Apricot and Almond Loaf

This moist, fruity loaf is packed with fibre, so, as mentioned above, it's useful if you're troubled by constipation during pregnancy or in the days following the birth. This loaf also contains protein and is a good source of calcium, iron and B vitamins.

MAKES ONE 450-G (1-LB) LOAF, CUTTING INTO 10 SLICES

125g (4 oz) dried apricots
150ml (¼ pint) hot water
125g (4 oz) plain wholewheat
  flour
1 teaspoon baking powder
½ teaspoon mixed spice
25g (1 oz) bran

125g (4 oz) sultanas
75g (3 oz) dark or light real
  barbados sugar
50g (2 oz) almonds, with skins
  on, chopped
1 egg

Wash apricots in warm water, then shred into small pieces with kitchen scissors or a sharp knife. Put into a bowl and cover with the hot water. Next day, set oven to 180°C (350°F), gas mark 4, and line a 450-g (1-lb) loaf tin with a strip of non-stick or greaseproof paper and grease well. Then sift the flour, baking powder and spice into another bowl and add the bran, sultanas, sugar, almonds and egg. Now add the apricots, together with the soaking water, and mix everything together well. Spoon into prepared tin. Bake in the centre of the oven for 50–60 minutes, until top springs back when touched, and a skewer inserted in the middle comes out clean. Turn out on to a wire rack to cool. Serve in thick slices, with butter.

If you don't eat dairy produce Omit the egg, increase the baking powder to 2 teaspoons and use 200ml (7 fl oz) hot water. Make sure the water has cooled to tepid before you add it to the rest of the ingredients.

To freeze When completely cold, wrap in polythene, label and freeze. To use, remove wrappings and stand loaf on a wire rack until defrosted.

Date Slices

These are a good source of iron and B vitamins and are particularly satisfying. They also make a good pudding, eaten warm from the oven with some milk, cream, all of the toppings on pages 181–3, or a dollop of natural yoghurt over them.

MAKES 16

225g (8 oz) cheapest dates –
  not the 'sugar-rolled' type
150ml (5 fl oz) water
175g (6 oz) plain wholewheat
  flour

175g (6 oz) porridge oats
175g (6 oz) polyunsaturated
  margarine
75g (3 oz) real demerara sugar
2 tablespoons cold water

Set oven to 190°C (375°F), gas mark 5. Grease a 20×30cm (7¾×12 in) swiss roll tin. Put the dates into a saucepan with the water and heat gently for 5–10 minutes, until the dates are mushy. Remove from the heat and mash with a spoon to make a thick purée, looking out for and removing any stones as you do so. Then leave on one side to cool. Meanwhile sift the flour into a bowl, adding also the residue of bran from the sieve and the oats. Rub in the margarine with your fingertips, then add the sugar and water, and press mixture together to form a dough. Press half this mixture into the greased tin, spread the cooled date purée on top, then cover evenly with the remaining oat mixture and press down gently but firmly. Bake for 30 minutes. Cool in tin, then mark into sections and remove with a spatula.

To freeze Pack in a rigid container with freezer paper between the layers; label and freeze. To use, remove from container as required. They defrost very quickly; can be eaten almost immediately.

Date and Walnut Loaf

Another loaf with plenty of fibre, so a useful cure for constipation problems in pregnancy and after the birth. This loaf is also a good source of B vitamins and is fatless.

MAKES ONE 450-G (1-LB) LOAF

175g (6 oz) dates
275ml (10 fl oz) water
50g (2 oz) barbados molasses
    sugar – from health shops
175g (6 oz) plain wholewheat
    flour

3 teaspoons baking powder
75g (3 oz) walnuts, chopped
1 teaspoon vanilla extract

Put dates into a saucepan with the water and simmer gently until dates are reduced to a mush. Remove from heat and leave on one side to cool. Set oven to 180°C (350°F), gas mark 4. Line a 450-g (1-lb) loaf tin with a strip of non-stick paper and grease. Sift flour and baking powder into a bowl, adding the residue of bran from the sieve too. Then add the walnuts, vanilla and cooled date mixture and stir well. Spoon into tin, bake for 50–60 minutes, until centre feels springy and a skewer inserted into the centre comes out clean. Cool on a wire rack. Serve cut into thick slices, and buttered if liked.

To freeze When completely cold, wrap in polythene, label and freeze. To use, remove wrappings and place loaf on a wire rack until defrosted.

Wholewheat Fruit Cake

This fruit cake contains good quantities of iron, calcium, B vitamins and fibre. It's a particularly good one to have in the early days of breast-feeding and will keep well in a tin for 3–4 weeks.

MAKES ONE 18-CM (7-IN) CAKE

300g (10 oz) plain wholewheat flour
2 teaspoons baking powder
150g (6 oz) polyunsaturated margarine
150g (6 oz) barbados molasses sugar – from health shops
3 eggs

450g (1 lb) mixed dried fruit
50g (2 oz) glacé cherries, washed and quartered, optional
grated rind of ½ a lemon
grated rind of ½ an orange
50g (2 oz) ground almonds
25g (1 oz) flaked almonds

Set oven to 160°C (325°F), gas mark 3. Grease an 18-cm (7-in) round cake tin and line with greased greaseproof paper. Sift the flour and baking powder into a large bowl, tipping in the bran from the sieve too. Then put in all the remaining ingredients except for the flaked almonds. Beat together with a wooden spoon (or in a mixer) for 2 minutes, until light and slightly glossy-looking. Spoon mixture into tin, level top, sprinkle with flaked almonds. Bake for 2¼–2½ hours, until a skewer inserted in the centre comes out clean. Let cake cool for 15 minutes or so in the tin, then turn out on to a wire rack, strip off paper and leave until completely cold. Store in an airtight tin.

To freeze Wrap cake in polythene, label and store for up to 3 months. To use, unwrap and stand cake on a wire cooling rack for 3–4 hours, until defrosted.

Fruit Cake without Eggs

The eggless fruit cake is light and delicious. Like the preceding recipe, this cake is nutritious and good for the early breast-feeding days.

MAKES ONE 18-CM (7-IN) CAKE

225g (8 oz) plain wholewheat flour
2 teaspoons baking powder
1 teaspoon mixed spice
150g (6 oz) barbados molasses sugar – from health shops
6 tablespoons oil
450g (1 lb) mixed dried fruit

50g (2 oz) glacé cherries, washed and quartered, optional
25g (1 oz) soya flour
25g (1 oz) ground almonds
225ml (8 fl oz) water
25g (1 oz) flaked almonds

Set oven to 160°C (325°F), gas mark 3. Grease an 18-cm (7-in) round cake tin and line with greased greaseproof paper. Sift the flour, baking powder and spice into a large bowl, tipping in the bran from the sieve too. Then put in all the remaining ingredients except for the flaked almonds. Beat together with a wooden spoon (or in a mixer) for 2 minutes, then spoon mixture into tin and sprinkle with flaked almonds. Bake for about 2¼ hours, until a skewer inserted in the centre comes out clean. Let cake cool for 15 minutes in the tin, then turn out on to a wire rack, strip off paper and leave until completely cold. Store in an airtight tin.

To freeze Wrap cake in polythene, label and store for up to 3 months. To use, unwrap and stand cake on a wire cooling rack for 3–4 hours, until defrosted.

Fruit Slices

Easy to make, with a delicious topping of iron-rich crunchy almonds.

MAKES 10–12

50g (2 oz) polyunsaturated margarine
50g (2 oz) barbados molasses sugar – from health shops
1 egg

125g (4 oz) wholewheat flour
225g (8 oz) mixed dried fruit
4 tablespoons water
40g (1½ oz) flaked almonds

Set oven to 160°C (325°F), gas mark 3. Line a 20-cm (8-in) square tin with non-stick or greaseproof paper and grease. Put the margarine and sugar into a bowl and cream together, then beat in the egg. Add the flour, dried fruit and water. Mix to a firm consistency which will drop heavily from the spoon when it's tapped against the side of the bowl. If necessary, add a little more water. Spoon mixture into the tin, level the top, sprinkle with flaked almonds. Bake for about 45 minutes, until the cake feels firm in the centre. Cool on a wire rack. Cut into ten or twelve pieces when cold.

To freeze Pack, label and store for up to 2 months. To use, unwrap and spread out on a wire cooling rack for 1–2 hours.

Parkin

Oatmeal is a natural remedy for depression and both molasses and wholewheat flour contain iron. So parkin, which contains both, is useful during pregnancy and afterwards as an antidote to postnatal depression or 'baby blues'. If you like the flavour of molasses you could further increase the iron content by using 2 heaped tablespoons molasses and leaving out the honey or golden syrup.

MAKES ONE 20-CM (8-IN) SQUARE CUTTING INTO 12

125g (4 oz) plain wholewheat flour	125g (4 oz) polyunsaturated margarine
2 teaspoons baking powder	1 big tablespoon molasses
2 teaspoons ground ginger	1 big tablespoon clear honey or golden syrup
125g (4 oz) medium oatmeal	175ml (6 fl oz) milk
125g (4 oz) real brown sugar	

Set oven to 180°C (350°F), gas mark 4. Grease and line a 20-cm (8-in) square tin with greased greaseproof paper. Sift the wholewheat flour, baking powder and ginger into a bowl, adding also the residue of bran from the sieve and the oatmeal. Put the sugar, margarine, molasses and honey into a pan and melt over a gentle heat. Cool until you can place your hand against the pan, then add to the flour mixture together with the milk. Mix well, then pour into prepared tin. Bake for 1 hour, until parkin feels set in the centre. Cool in tin, then turn out and strip off paper. Cut into pieces. Store in an airtight tin. The parkin may sink a bit in the centre as it cools, but it has a wonderful, moist, gooey texture and no hard 'crust' on top.

If you don't eat dairy produce Replace milk with soya milk.

To freeze Freeze in a rigid container. To use, remove slices as needed, place on a wire rack until defrosted: this does not take very long.

Wholewheat Scones with Raisins and Molasses

These scones have a delicious flavour and a light, crumbly texture. They're a good source of iron and are nice to eat just as they are, or with butter.

MAKES 8

125g (4 oz) plain wholewheat flour
2 teaspoons baking powder
25g (1 oz) polyunsaturated margarine
25g (1 oz) light barbados sugar – from health shops

1 tablespoon fine or medium oatmeal
25g (1 oz) raisins
1 tablespoon molasses
4 tablespoons milk or soya milk

Set oven to 180°C (350°F), gas mark 4. Sift the flour and baking powder into a bowl, adding the bran from the sieve, too. Rub in the margarine with your fingertips, then add the sugar, oatmeal and raisins. Mix together the molasses and milk, then add to the rest of the ingredients and mix gently to form a dough. Turn dough out on to lightly floured board, knead lightly and form into a circle. Place circle on a floured baking sheet and score it across into eight sections. Bake for 15 minutes. Cool in the tin, then transfer to a cooling rack.

If you don't eat dairy produce Replace milk with soya milk.

Variation The raisins can be omitted, or replaced with other dried fruit such as sultanas or chopped dates.

To freeze This freezes well. Wrap in polythene, label, freeze. To use, remove wrappings, stand scone ring on wire rack for about 60 minutes to defrost. Or freeze in individual sections, which can be taken out as required and defrost in about 15 minutes.

Crunchy Bars

Crisp and delicious, these are also a good source of calcium, iron and protein. They're useful for taking to the hospital when you have the baby and the oats are helpful for counteracting 'baby blues'.

MAKES 16

125g (4 oz) rolled oats
125g (4 oz) plain wholewheat flour
125g (4 oz) real demerara sugar – from health shops
1 tablespoon clear honey

150ml (5 fl oz) oil
40g (1½ oz) flaked almonds or roasted peanuts (see page 154), lightly chopped
2 teaspoons vanilla essence
2 tablespoons sesame seeds

Set oven to 200°C (400°F), gas mark 6. Grease a 20×30cm (7¾×12 in) swiss roll in. Put all the ingredients into a bowl and mix together. Spread in tin. Bake for 15–17 minutes, until golden brown. Mark into slices, cool in tin. When completely cold, store in an airtight tin.

To freeze Pack in a rigid container, label, freeze. Remove as required; these defreeze very quickly and can be eaten within a few minutes.

Oatmeal Biscuits

This is another way of taking oats, which, as mentioned before, are a traditional herbal remedy for depression. These are plain biscuits which are nice with butter and/or cheese, though I also like them just as they are.

100g (4 oz) fine or medium
oatmeal

100g (4 oz) plain 100 per cent
wholewheat flour

1 teaspoon baking powder

100g (4 oz) butter or
margarine

1 tablespoon real demerara
sugar

2 tablespoons water

extra oatmeal for rolling out

Set oven to 180°C (350°F), gas mark 4. Put oats, flour and baking powder into a bowl and rub in the butter. Add the sugar and water to mix to a dough. Sprinkle some oatmeal on a board or clean working surface and roll out the dough 6 mm (⅛ in) thick. Cut into 7-cm (2¾-in) circles, place on baking sheet, prick lightly. Bake for 20 minutes. Cool slightly on baking sheet, then transfer to a wire tray. Store in an airtight tin.

To freeze Cook completely, cool. Pack in a rigid container. Freeze for 2–3 months. To use, remove from container, spread out on wire tray for about 15 minutes.

HEALTHY SWEETS

It's important to keep up your energy level when you're pregnant and breast-feeding, and something sweet is very appealing, but you obviously do not want to eat sweets which are virtually all sugar and fat, with no goodness. So I have included these easy to make, nutritious sweets, which you can take to hospital for eating after the baby is born and keep by you while you're breast-feeding. Although these contain some sweeteners, they are kept to the minimum and are balanced by the other highly nutritious ingredients which are used.

Carob Fudge

This is semi-sweet and chewy. It's quite a pleasant way to take the molasses and wheat germ supplement suggested on page 20.

MAKES 12-15 SQUARES

25g (1 oz) hard vegetable margarine such as Tomor, or hard vegetable fat such as Nutter – both from health shops
25g (1 oz) chopped figs
25g (1 oz) molasses

1 rounded tablespoon wheat germ
25g (1 oz) grated or ground almonds
25g (1 oz) carob powder
1 teaspoon vanilla extract

Melt the margarine and add the figs; cook over a gentle heat for a few minutes, until figs are softened. Then stir in the molasses. Cook for a moment or two longer, then remove from the heat and beat in all the remaining ingredients. Press mixture into a shallow tin. Leave until cold and set. Cut into squares.

Date Knobs

No extra sugar in this recipe, which is rich in fibre, iron, calcium and B vitamins.

MAKES 24

50g (2 oz) dried apricots
125g (4 oz) cheapest dates (not 'sugar-rolled')
125g (4 oz) seeded raisins

125g (4 oz) nuts: almonds, brazil nuts, roasted peanuts (see page 154)
2–3 tablespoons orange juice

Wash apricots well in warm water, then chop. Chop raisins and nuts finely – the easiest way is to use a blender or food processor.

Mix everything together, adding a little orange juice to make a dough-like consistency. Press mixture into a lightly greased tin, making it about 1cm (½ in) deep. Chill, then cut into squares.

To freeze Place in rigid container; label and freeze. Take out individually as required: they can be eaten within a few minutes.

Fruit and Nut Bars

A pleasant and nutritious recipe, especially rich in calcium, iron and B vitamins.

MAKES 16

75g (3 oz) dried apricots	50g (2 oz) desiccated coconut
175g (6 oz) dates	50g (2 oz) ground almonds
150g (5 oz) dried figs	grated rind of 1 orange or
2–3 tablespoons orange juice	lemon
50g (2 oz) desiccated coconut	extra desiccated coconut

Wash the apricots thoroughly, then chop all the dried fruit – a food processor is good for this. Then add the juice, coconut, almonds and grated rind. Press mixture into lightly greased 20-cm (8-in) square shallow tin, making it about 1cm (1½ in) deep. Sprinkle with more desiccated coconut. Chill, then cut into oblongs.

To freeze Place in rigid container; label and freeze. Take out individually as required: they can be eaten within a few minutes.

Molasses Sweets with Fruit and Nuts

Pleasant sweetmeats which are rich in iron.

MAKES 12

75g (3 oz) sunflower seeds
1 tablespoon honey
1 tablespoon molasses
25g (1 oz) carob powder
1 teaspoon vanilla

1 teaspoon vanilla
25g (1 oz) raisins or sultanas
25g (1 oz) roasted peanuts (see page 154)
extra carob for coating

Grind sunflower seeds to a powder in a blender or food processor then add the honey, molasses and carob and mix well. Then mix in all the remaining ingredients, to make a paste. Roll into balls and coat in carob powder.

Baby Foods

As mentioned earlier, on the whole I'm not in favour of preparing special foods for the baby; I think it's far better to get the baby used to family food from the beginning. Many of the recipes given in the preceding sections of this book are suitable for the baby. Where a recipe is definitely unsuitable, usually because it is too spicy, I have mentioned this, and I have also suggested ways in which recipes can be adapted for a baby if necessary.

However, having said this, there are one or two dishes which are particularly suitable for a baby, and I have included them in this chapter. First, though, one or two general points about preparing food for a baby.

It's best not to add either salt or spices to the baby's food (spices can lead to dehydration, and taking too much salt, especially at an early age, can increase the risk of high blood pressure later on). So, if the baby is going to share some of the family's food, take the baby's portion out before adding seasoning.

Similarly, babies are better off without sugar. Use a purée of dates (see page 209) or other dried fruits to take the sharpness off something like stewed apple or natural yoghurt. Also try to keep the food as low in fat as possible: plump toddlers can often be 'slimmed' painlessly simply by reducing their fat intake.

Of course it goes without saying that baby food should be prepared as hygienically as possible, and baby foods for the freezer should be cooled and frozen quickly.

Apricot Purée

This mixture keeps well in the fridge or can be frozen in ice-cube containers.

MAKES ABOUT 4 BABY-PORTIONS

125g (4 oz) dried apricots, well washed
boiling water

Cover the apricots with water and leave to soak for several hours. Then transfer apricots and water to a saucepan and cook gently for about 30 minutes, until very tender. Liquidize or sieve.

Baby's Baked Beans

A quick, 'emergency' meal, which my youngest daughter loved.

SERVES 1

½ piece wholewheat bread, crusts removed
1 tablespoon boiling water
1 tablespoon baked beans

You can make this straight into the baby's bowl. Put all the ingredients into the bowl and mash together. The boiling water will make the mixture warm enough to give straight to the baby.

Date Purée

This is useful for sweetening yoghurt and other puddings, also for spreading on fingers of bread and butter or toast. It keeps for at least a fortnight in a jar in the fridge.

MAKES 225G (8 OZ)

125g (4 oz) cheapest dates – not 'sugar-rolled'
150ml (5 fl oz) water

Chop the dates roughly, removing any stones or hard pieces. Put dates into a small saucepan with the water and heat gently for 5–10 minutes, until soft. Beat to a purée with a wooden spoon.

Ground Rice

1 teaspoon ground brown rice or rice flour, from health shops
75ml (3 fl oz) milk or soy milk
date purée, see above, to sweeten, or 2 tablespoons finely grated
    cheese or pulverized nuts

Blend the ground rice to a cream with some of the milk. Heat the rest of the milk, then add this to the ground rice cream, stir and return to the pan. Heat gently, stirring often, for 5–10 minutes. This can be sweetened with date purée and served as a pudding or breakfast dish, or made into a savoury with the addition of grated cheese or nuts.

Lentil Purée

1 small onion, peeled and finely chopped
1 small carrot, scraped and finely chopped
2 teaspoons oil
25g (1 oz) split red lentils
150ml (5 fl oz) water

Fry the onion and carrot lightly in the oil for 10 minutes. Then add the lentils and water. Cook gently, covered, for 15–20 minutes, until lentils are soft. Liquidize. This can be thinned with a little milk.

Millet Cream

If you can get flaked millet at the health shop, this can be used in exactly the same way as ground brown rice, page 209. It comes out an attractive golden colour which can be enhanced by the addition of an egg yolk, if you eat dairy produce.

Baby Muesli

For this recipe and the next one, it's a good idea to powder a quantity of rolled oats by whizzing them in the liquidizer or food processor – it's easier to do a quantity at a time.

SERVES 1

1 tablespoon finely grated apple
2 teaspoons rolled oats, whizzed to a powder in a liquidizer
2 tablespoons milk
1 teaspoon date purée (page 209)
2 teaspoons finely powdered nuts

Just mix everything together.

Baby's Nut Meat

SERVES 1

½ piece wholewheat bread, crusts removed
2 tablespoons boiling water
1 tablespoon finely powdered almonds

Mix everything together, beating well to break up the bread.

Porridge

Make this as described for ground rice, page 209, using oats which have been powdered as described on page 210. Makes a good breakfast for a baby.

Potato Lunch

MAKES 1 BABY-PORTION

50g (2 oz) potato, scrubbed
1 tablespoon milk
optional extra ingredients: 1 tablespoon cottage cheese, grated cheese, finely grated nuts, very finely grated raw carrot, very finely chopped parsley, watercress or raw spinach

Boil the potato in its skin until tender. Remove skin and mash potato with the milk. This is very nutritious as it is, though any of the additional ingredients can be added for extra nourishment and interest.

Rusks

4–6 slices wholewheat bread

Set oven to 160°C (325°F), gas mark 3. Remove crusts from bread, then cut the bread into suitably sized pieces. Spread pieces of bread out on a dry baking tray. Bake for about 30 minutes, until crisp and golden brown. Cool. These keep well in an airtight tin.

Semolina Cheese

Make this from wholewheat semolina, which you can get from health shops, exactly as described for ground brown rice, page 209.

Useful Addresses

The National Childbirth Trust (NCT), 9 Queensborough Terrace, London W2 3TB.

The Vegetarian Society, 53 Marloes Road, London W8.

The Vegan Society, 47 Highlands Road, Leatherhead, Surrey KT22 8NQ.

Foresight, The Association for the Promotion of Preconceptual Care, The Old Vicarage, Witley, Surrey. I think it is a pity that this association has rather a negative attitude towards vegetarianism.

For information on the pros and cons of screening tests

The Medical Education Trust (Secretary), 75 St Mary's Road, Huyton, Merseyside L36 5SR.

For advice and help on getting a home confinement

Society for the Support of Home Confinement, c/o Margaret White, 17 Laburnum Avenue, Durham.

Association of Radical Midwives, Lakefield, 8a The Drive, Wimbledon, London SW19.

Association for the Improvement of the Maternity Services, 19 Allerton Grange Crescent, Chapel Allerton, Leeds LS17 6LN.

For information on getting raspberry leaf, lime (sometimes called linden flower) and meadowsweet tea, as mentioned on page 113

Culpeper Ltd, Hadstock Road, Linton, Cambridge.

For an astrological character analysis, as mentioned on page 93

Send name, date, time and place of birth and £10 to: Rose Elliot Horoscopes, The Old Rectory, Bishopstoke, Eastleigh, Hampshire SO5 6BH, or write for further details.

Further Reading

ON NUTRITION

Eating Well for a Healthy Pregnancy by Dr Barbara M. Pickard (Sheldon Press) is very helpful. Dr Pickard is an honorary research Fellow in the Department of Animal Physiology and Nutrition at the University of Leeds, and has also published two useful pamphlets 'Are you fit enough to become pregnant?', and 'Nausea and vomiting in early pregnancy'. These pamphlets are available, price 50p and 80p respectively, from Dr B. M. Pickard, Lane End Farm, Dewton, Ilkley, Yorkshire LS29 0HP. I particularly like Dr Pickard's writing, which is understanding and informative.

I'd also like to recommend, if I may, three of my own cookery books which I think might be especially helpful for quick, healthy meals. They are *Simply Delicious*, *Not Just a Load of Old Lentils* and *Your Very Good Health*; all published in paperback by Fontana.

ON PREGNANCY AND CHILDBIRTH

Birthrights: a Parents' Guide to Modern Childbirth by Sally Inch (Hutchinson) is a most useful reference book which gives detailed information on the different types of birth, tests, and how to go about getting a home confinement. I have special affection for Erna Wright's *The New Childbirth* (Tandem). It was published a few weeks before my first baby was born and I know that it was reading this book and practising the exercises described which helped to make her birth such a wonderful experience. Like all Sheila Kitzinger's books, *Birth Over Thirty* (Sheldon Press) is full of useful information presented in a highly readable and understanding way.

ON BREAST-FEEDING
Two excellent pamphlets by the NCT (for address, see page 213) are 'Breast-feeding – a Good Start' and 'Breast-feeding – Avoiding some of the Difficulties'. *The Breast-feeding Book* by Marie Messenger (Century) is written by a mother and NCT breast-feeding counsellor, and is a particularly attractive and helpful book. *The Experience of Breast-feeding* by Sheila Kitzinger (Pelican). *Breast is Best* by Drs Penny and Andrew Stanway (Pan) has become a 'classic' on breast-feeding. The La Leche League of Great Britain has some very useful advice on breast-feeding. The address is: The La Leche League, Great Britain, BN3424, London WC1N 3XX. Tel: (01) 242 1278.

MISCELLANEOUS
Barbara Griggs's *The Home Herbal* (Pan) is a useful and interesting book of simple herbal remedies for common ailments.

ON BABY AND CHILD CARE
Baby and Child by Penelope Leach (Penguin) is my favourite book on child care; sensitive, practical and informative.

Index

Addresses, useful 213
Allergies 83–4
Almond
  cream, cashew nut or 182–3
  and mushroom nutmeat, quick 171–2
  spread, peanut or 134
  topping, creamy tofu and 181–2
Amino acids 16–17
Amniocentesis 38
Antenatal
  care 37–8
  classes 46–7
Apple(s)
  healthy baked 183–4
  and raisin compote 184
Apricot
  and almond loaf, bran 193–4
  with cashew nut cream 184–5
  fool 185–6
  orange and almond whizz 107–8
  and orange nectar 108
  purée 208
Avena Sativa Compound 90
Avocado, watercress and walnut salad 121–2

B vitamins, requirements and sources 23–7
B₁₂ 26–7
Baby
  3–6 months 72–6
  6–12 months 77–91
  12–24 months 92–102
  clothes, buying 41–3

emotional needs 81
foods 207–12
foods, preparation of 207
muesli 210
play and development 93–6
safety precautions 77–9
Baby's
  baked beans 208
  nut meat 211
Bake
  buckwheat 139–40
  rice, tomato and cashew nut 148
Baked
  apples, healthy 183–4
  beans, baby's 208
  potatoes with various toppings 175
Balanced diet, creating a 28–9
Banana
  and crunchy granola, yoghurt and 190
  milk shake 109
Bean
  and lentil dishes 166–71
  salad, mixed 122
  spread 130–1
Beans, baby's baked 208
Beetroot, orange and cottage cheese salad 123
Biotin 26
Birth and the first few days 51–60
Biscuits, oatmeal 202–3
Borsch, easy 114–15
Bottle-feeding 57–60
  choosing type of milk 58–9
  equipment for 58

Bottle-feeding [*cont'd*]
  giving the feed 59
  making up feeds 59
Bran, apricot and almond loaf 193–4
Bras, nursing 39–41
Breast-feeding
  bras and clothes for 39–41
  establishing 54–7
  expressing milk 55–6
  the first feed 52–3
  increasing supply of milk 67–9
  preparations for 38–9
Breathing, NCT 51–2
Brown rice with tomatoes and nuts 156
Buckwheat
  bake 139–40
  with mushrooms, onions and tomatoes 158
Bulgur wheat
  with peach and raisin sauce 160
  pilaf with red peppers, nuts and onions 159
Burping the baby 60
Butter bean(s)
  pie, vegetable and 151
  quick curried 166–7
  and tomato soup 115–16

Cabbage salad, main course 123–4
Cake(s)
  biscuits and sweets 192–206
  wholewheat fruit 197
  without eggs, fruit 198
Calcium, requirements and sources of 21–3
Carob
  fudge 204
  shake 109
Carrot slices 142
Cashew nut
  bake, rice, tomato and 148
  or almond cream 182–3
  cream, apricots with 184–5
Cauliflower
  cheese, easy 172

with peanut and tomato sauce 173
Cereal dishes 156–66
Cereals 153
Cheese 152–3
  easy cauliflower 172
  sauce 138–9
  spread 131–2
  tomato and onion flan 161
  vegan 133–4
Cheesecake, easy uncooked non-dairy 186
Cheesy lentils, easy 169
Chickpeas, creamed, with croutons 167–8
Chilli red beans 168
Chunky nut and vegetable roast 143
Clothes
  baby, how to choose 41–3
  for breast-feeding 39–41
  for toddlers 93
Colic, evening 69–70
Colostrum 54–5
Complementary protein 16–17
Compote
  apple and raisin 184
  dried fruit 187
Constipation 33
Coping
  during the day 62–6
  in the early days, 0–3 months 61–71
  during the evening 67–70
  at night 70–1
Cottage cheese salad, beetroot, orange and 123
Cradling, the first 52
Cream
  cashew nut or almond 182–3
  millet 210
Creamy chickpeas with croutons 167–8
Creamed tofu and almond topping 181–2
Crunchy
  bars 202
  sesame topping 183
Curried butter beans, quick 166

Curried soya bean and apple spread 132
Curry sauce, spiced brown rice with 156–7
Cutlets, lentil and onion 146

Date
  knobs 204–5
  purée 209
  slices 195
  and walnut loaf 196
Dips and spreads 130–4
Discipline and punishment 96–7
Domino System 36
Dressing
  tofu 120
  yoghurt 119–20
Dried fruit compote 187
Drinks 107–13
Dummy, use of 65, 69

Early days, 0–3 months, coping 61–71
Easy
  borsch 114–15
  cauliflower cheese 172
  cheesy lentils 169
  ratatouille 178
  uncooked non-dairy cheesecake 186
Eating plans, 9–12 months 86–7
Eggs 152
Emotional needs 81
Equipment
  baby bath 46
  chairs and high chairs 45
  cots, prams and pushchairs 43–4
  general 43–6
  nappy changing and washing 45–6
  slings and carriers 44–5
Expressing breast milk 55–6

Father's role 49–50
Feed, the first 52–3
Feeding
  bottle *see* bottle-feeding
  breast *see* breast-feeding
Feeding problems 87–8
Figs with yoghurt and sesame seeds 187

Flan
  cheese, tomato and onion 161
  mushroom, with tofu 163–4
Flip, yoghurt and orange 112
Folic acid 25–6
Food cravings 32
Foods to be avoided 32
Fortified milk 10
Freezer
  preparing breadcrumbs for 136
  preparing pulses for 135–6
  sauces for 137–9
  savouries 139–51
Fritters, tofu, with lemon 170–1
Fruit
  cake, wholewheat 197
  cake, without eggs 198
  and nut bars 205
  salad 188
  slices 199
Fudge, carob 204
Further Reading 214–15

GP Unit 36
Grated swede salad 127
Gravy, vegetarian 137
Greek salad 124–5
Ground rice 209

Hazel nut
  spread 132–3
  and vegetable pasties 144
Healthy
  baked apples 183–4
  sweets 203–6
Heartburn 33
Herb teas 113
Home delivery 36
Homemade peanut butter 133
Hummus 131

Ingredients
  for cakes, biscuits and sweets 192–3
  choice of 105
  for quick meals 152–5

Introductions 11, 105
Iodine 28
Iron, requirements and sources of 17–21

Knobs, date 204–5

Lassi 110–11
Leboyer, Frederick 35
Leek
  and potato pie 145
  and potato soup, thick 116–17
Lentil(s)
  dishes, bean and 166–71
  easy cheesy 169
  and onion cutlets 146
  and potatoes, spicy 169–70
  purée 210
  and red pepper sauce, pasta with 164–5
  soup, main course 117–18
  split red 154
Loaf
  bran, apricot and almond 193–4
  date and walnut 196
  soya and walnut 150

Magnesium 27–8
Main course
  cabbage salad 123–4
  cereal, pastry and pasta dishes, quick, 156–66
  lentil soup 117–18
  mashed potatoes 178
  meals, quick 152–80
  vegetable and nut dishes 171–80
Mashed potatoes, main course 178
Mealtimes 101–2
Menu-building 29–31
Milk
  fortified 110
  shake, banana 109
Millet
  cream 210

pilaf with almonds (or peanuts) and tomato sauce 162–3
pilaf with mixed vegetables 162–3
Miso pick-me-up 111
Mixed
  bean salad 122
  nut roast 147
Molasses sweets with fruit and nuts 206
Morning sickness 32
Muesli
  baby 210
  oaty version 189–90
  original version 188–9
Mushroom(s)
  flan with tofu 163–4
  onions and tomatoes, buckwheat with 158

Nectar, apricot and orange 108
Niacin *see* nicotinic acid
Nicotinic acid 25
Nightmares 99
Nipples, sore 53, 56–7
Non-dairy cheesecake, easy uncooked 186
Nut
  dishes, main course vegetable and, 171–80
  meat, baby's 211
  rissoles, quick 174
  roast, chunky, and vegetable 143
  roast, mixed 147
Nutmeat, quick almond and mushroom 171–2
Nuts and seeds 154

Oatmeal biscuits 202–3
Odent, Michel 35
Orange
  and almond whizz, apricot 107–8
  and cottage cheese salad, beetroot 123
  flip, yoghurt and 112
  nectar, apricot and 108
Organizing the home 47–8

Packed meals 129–34
Packing for hospital 26
Pantothenic acid 48–9
Parkin 200
Parsley sauce 138
Pasta
  with lentil and red pepper sauce 164–5
  rings, wholewheat, with tomato sauce 165
  wholewheat 155
Pasties, hazel nut and vegetable 144
Peach and raisin sauce, bulgur wheat with 160
Peanut and tomato sauce, cauliflower with 173
Peanut(s)
  butter, homemade 133
  spread, almond or 134
  to roast 154
Peel Report 36
Pick-me-up, miso 111
Pie
  leek and potato 145
  vegetable and butter bean 151
Pilaf
  bulgur wheat, with red peppers, nuts and onions 159
  millet, with almonds (or peanuts) and tomato sauce 162–3
  millet, with mixed vegatbles 162–3
Piles 33
Pizza, quick 166
Place of birth, choosing 35–7
Porridge 211
Potato(es)
  cakes with nuts or sunflower seeds 176
  lunch 211
  main course mashed 178
  pie, leek and 145
  soup, thick leek and 116–17
  spicy lentils and 169–70
Pregnancy
  healthy diet for 13–34

preparations for the birth 35–50
Protein, requirement and sources of 14–17
Puddings 181–91
Pulses
  how to cook and freeze 135–6
  for quick meals 153–4
Purée
  apricot 208
  date 209
  lentil 210
Pyridoxine 25

Quick
  almond and mushroom nutmeat 171–2
  curried butter beans 166
  main meals 152–80
  meals, ingredients for 152–5
  nut rissoles 174
  pizza 166

Raisin compote, apple and 184
Ratatouille, easy 178
Recipes
  choice of 106
  choice of ingredients for 105
  introduction 105–6
Red beans, chilli 168
Rest and sleep 98–9
Riboflavin 24–5
Rice
  ground 209
  spiced brown with curry sauce 156–7
  tomato and cashew nut bake 148
  with tomatoes and nuts 156
Rissoles, quick nut 174
Rooming-in 35–6, 54–7
Rusks 212

Safety precautions 77–9
Salad(s) 119–28
  bowl, vitality 128
  dressings 119–20
  avocado, watercress and walnut 121–2

Salad(s) [*cont'd*]
  beetroot, orange and cottage cheese 123
  fruit 188
  grated swede 127
  Greek 124–5
  main course cabbage 123–4
  mixed bean 122
  soya bean 125–6
  spinach 126
Sandwich fillings
  savoury 130
  sweet 129
Sauce(s)
  cheese 138–9
  for freezer 137–9
  parsley 138
  tomato 139
  white, and variations 138–9
Sausages, soya 149
Savouries, freezer 139–51
Scones, wholewheat, with raisins and molasses 201
Semolina cheese 212
Sesame topping, crunchy 183
Shake
  banana milk 109
  carob 109
Sleeping, 6–12 months 88–91
Slices
  date 195
  fruit 199
Sore nipples 53, 56–7
Soup(s) 114–18
  butter bean and tomato, 115–16
  main course lentil 117–18
  thick leek and potato 116–17
  watercress 118
Soya
  sausages 149
  and walnut loaf 150
Soya bean
  and apple spread, curried 132
  salad 125–6

Spiced brown rice with curry sauce 156–7
Spicy lentils and potatoes 169–70
Spinach salad 126
Split red lentils 154
Spread
  bean 130–1
  cheese 131–2
  curried soya bean and apple 132
  hazel nut 132–3
  peanut or almond 134
Sprouting beans and seeds 121
Stew, vegetable 180
Stir-fried vegetables 179
Swede salad, grated 127
Sweets
  healthy 203–6
  molasses, with fruit and nuts 206

Tabbouleh 127–8
Tantrums, coping with 97–8
Teething 75–6
Thiamine 24
Thick leek and potato soup 116–17
Timetable, for feeding, 56–7, 62
Tofu 153–4
  and almond topping, creamy 181–2
  dressing 120
  fritters with lemon 170–1
  mushroom flan with 163–4
  topping, whipped 182
Toilet training 99–101
Tomato(es)
  and nuts, brown rice with 156
  sauce 139
  soup, butter bean and 115–16
Top-and-tail, how to 65
Topping(s)
  creamy tofu and almond 181–2
  crunchy sesame 183
  for baked potatoes 175
  whipped tofu 182

Ultrasonic scan 37–8
Useful addresses 213

Vegan
  cheese 133–4
  definition of 13
  yoghurt 191
Vegetable(s)
  and butter bean pie 151
  easy 155
  and nut dishes, main courses 171–80
  pasties, hazel nut and 144
  roast, chunky nut and 143
  stew 180
  stir-fried 179
Vegetarian
  definition of 13
  gravy 137
Vitality salad bowl 128

Walnut loaf, soya and 150
Watercress
  soup 118
  and walnut salad, avocado 121–2

Weaning 81–7
Weight control 34
Whipped tofu topping 182
White sauce and variations 138–9
Whizz, apricot, orange and almond 107–8
Wholewheat
  breadcrumbs, freezing 136
  flour 154
  fruit cake 197
  pasta rings with tomato sauce 165
  scones with raisins and molasses 201

Yoghurt
  banana and crunchy granola 190
  dressing 119–20
  and orange flip 112
  and sesame seeds, figs with 187
  vegan 191

Zinc 27